Science
Experiments
with Sound

Books by Harry Sootin

Experiments in Magnetism and Electricity
Isaac Newton
Gregor Mendel: Father of Science and Genetics
Michael Faraday: From Errand Boy to Master Physicist
Robert Boyle: Founder of Modern Chemistry
Twelve Pioneers of Science
Experiments with Machines and Matter
Light Experiments, for Home Workshop and School Laboratory
Experiments with Heat

Science Experiments with Sound

by Harry Sootin

illustrated by Frank Aloise

34140

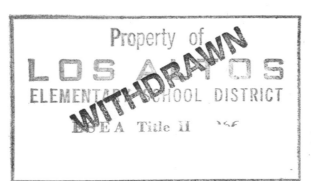

New York

W · W · Norton & Company · Inc ·

Contents

Foreword

The experiments in this book on sound are so arranged as to lead to definite ideas and principles relating to each of the subjects covered. It is therefore important that the text pages preceding each group of experiments be carefully studied both before and after the experiments are carried out. The materials needed are inexpensive, readily available, and easily put together. The emphasis throughout is on *understanding* rather than on construction of complicated devices or gadgets.

Laboratory experiences are invaluable to science students. They must be allowed to arrange simple apparatus, improvise, adjust, fumble, and wonder why "things happen." This kind of learning requires a quiet, unhurried atmosphere. Hence the experiments that follow might best be done at home during long, leisurely afternoons or evenings.

In recent years so much new subject matter has been added to science courses that there is simply no time during the school day for the student to "try things" by himself and at his own pace. This is unfortunate, for teachers are well aware that the laboratory approach to science is far superior to any other. It cannot — and should not — be replaced by lectures, films, TV, or classroom demonstrations.

To get the most out of this book, the reader should regard the material in it as a starting point, as an *introduction* to the study of sound. A deeper insight into many important scientific principles awaits those who make use of the reading list at the end of the book. It is hoped that the suggestions on page 89 will help guide inquiring minds towards this goal.

facts and ideas about . . .

Vibrations and Sound

You are going to clamp a long strip of steel or iron in a vise. You will pull the free end aside and let go. You will then count the back-and-forth movements executed by the strip in one minute, or in a convenient fraction of a minute.

Each back-and-forth movement is called a *vibration.* The number of *vibrations per second,* often written as vps, is called the *frequency.*

You will shorten the length of the vibrating steel strip and observe the change in the number of vibrations per minute. You will listen to the sound emitted by the vibrating strip. Does the shrillness or pitch of the sound increase as the frequency increases? Try it.

It will be difficult for you to count accurately the number of back-and-forth movements of the strip after you begin to shorten it. Why? You can, however, calculate the number of vibrations per second of the shortened strip.

Keep this in mind: If you make the length of the vibrating strip half as long, it will vibrate four times as frequently in a given time; if one-third as long, nine times as frequently; if one-fourth as long, sixteen times as frequently. In other words, the number of vibrations per second of your steel strip will vary *inversely* as the *square* of the length of the vibrating part.

Your vibrating strip sets up a train of pulses or waves in the air. These waves reach your eardrum, and then your brain, where they are translated into sounds. The human ear does not respond to frequencies that are too low or too high. The limits of audibility vary with different people; most people can hear sounds whose frequencies are between 20 and 20,000 vibrations per second.

Sounds below 20 vibrations per second (vps) or cycles per second (cps) are called *subsonic*. Sounds above 20,000 vps are called *ultrasonic*.

Think about this: Your finger supplied the force which disturbed the free part of the steel strip from its position of rest. This *displacement* was resisted by a *restoring* force which acted to bring the strip back to its rest position.

This restoring force acquired momentum, overshot its mark, and moved to a position on the opposite side of the rest position. Then another restoring force came into play, another overshooting resulted, etc. To maintain the back-and-forth movements, *elasticity* and *inertia* must be present. Look into this.

How can one find the number of vibrations per minute of the strip directly rather than by calculation? You could attach a thin wire to the free end of the strip. The vibrating wire will make a series of marks or waves on a smoked glass plate moved at *right angles* to the direction of vibration. If the smoked plate is moved with a known speed, the number of vibrations in a given time may then be counted.

Vibrations and Sound

1.

DO THIS: Place a long iron strip, about 3 or 4 feet long, 1/2 inch wide, and 1/16 inch thick, in a vise. Pull end aside. It will vibrate at a rate that can be counted. The clicking against a lightly held straw will help you count the vibrations.

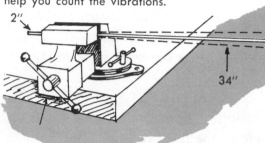

How many vibrations or clicks in 15 seconds? One minute? Make several trials and average your results. Do you hear any sound?

2.

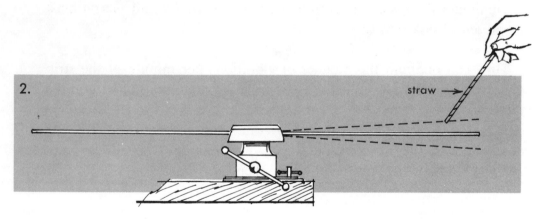

Now reduce the length of the vibrating part by half. If it was 34 inches before, make it 17 inches, etc.

How many vibrations in 15 seconds now? In one second? In one minute?

Is the strip now vibrating too quickly for you to count? Remember that when length is halved, the vibrations per second are multiplied by *four*. If you counted 3 vibrations per second above, you will now get 12 vibrations per second. Do you hear any sound?

NOTE: Long thin strips of iron are sold at most hardware stores, or use the thin steel rods called "music wire," sold at hobby shops.

3.

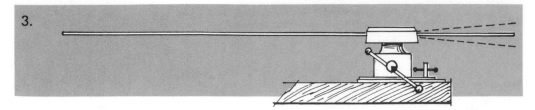

Keep reducing the length of the vibrating part of your strip. Does the sound become more audible? higher, shriller? Try a 6-inch length, a 3-inch length, etc.

4. How to calculate the vibrations per second when your vibrating strip is short — i.e., 2 inches long.

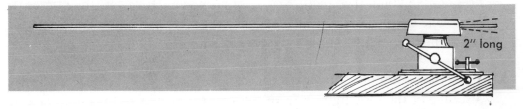

2″ long

Make use of the vibrations per second found when the strip was long and its to-and-fro movements easy to count. Also make use of this fact: the number of vibrations per second varies *inversely* as the *square* of the length.
This means: 1/2 the length will produce 4 times as many vps.
1/4 the length will produce 16 times as many vps.
1/10 the length will produce 100 times as many vps.
Suppose your strip vibrated 3 times per second when its length was 34 inches. Then for 2 inches, or 1/17 the length, it will vibrate 289 times per second faster, since 17 x 17 = 289. This means the vibration frequency at 2 inches is 289 greater than it was at 34 inches. Therefore 3 x 289 = 867 vps, frequency of your 2-inch strip.

facts and ideas about . . .

Making Traces of a Vibrating Body

You are going to attach an inky feather to a pendulum bob. You will extend the feather slightly beyond the bob, so that it will mark lines on paper when the pendulum moves back and forth.

While the pendulum is vibrating, you will move the paper with a *steady* speed at *right angles* to the direction in which the pendulum is vibrating. You will see a series of waves traced on the moving paper by the inky feather.

Do the curves you obtain look like water waves? Actually these waves *do not* give you a true picture of a sound wave. However, the curves do represent graphically the *displacement against time* of a body moving back and forth with simple harmonic motion.

As the pendulum bob moves back and forth the inky feather traces the distance of the moving bob from the neutral or rest position at each instant. The maximum displacement from the rest position is called the *amplitude* of the wave.

You will swing the pendulum through a small arc and then through a larger arc to see the effect on the wave traced by the feather. How does the amplitude of the wave change as the arc through which the bob moves changes?

Examine the waves traced by the inky feather on the paper. The distance from one *crest* to the next *crest,* or one *trough* to the next *trough,* is called a *wave length*. It is the length of a *complete wave*. You will try shortening your pendulum to make it swing faster — i.e., more vibrations per second. Does the wave length of your traced curve increase or decrease?

The *frequency* of a vibrating body is the number of vibrations it makes in one second.

The frequency of a train of waves is the number of complete waves that pass a stationary point in one second. In your experiment you will be able to observe only a few waves. Unless you know exactly how fast you move the paper, you cannot find the frequency of vibration from your trace.

You might try this: Shorten the length of your pendulum. Examine the trace on the moving paper. Since the pendulum is now vibrating more frequently per second, are more curves traced on the paper? Explain.

We shall study more about waves and wave forms in the next experiment. In the meantime remember that a truer picture of a sound wave is that of a series of expanding spherical waves spreading in all directions from the vibrating body. These moving spherical layers consist alternately of *condensations,* where the air molecules are compressed, and *rarefactions,* where the air molecules are moving apart.

How to Make Traces of a Vibrating Body

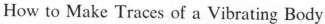

1.

light string

pendulum bob or any small heavy object

feather

barb from feather

cellophane tape

DO THIS: Remove one barb from a feather. Attach it to pendulum bob with cellophane tape as shown. Be sure end of barb extends about an inch below bob.

2.

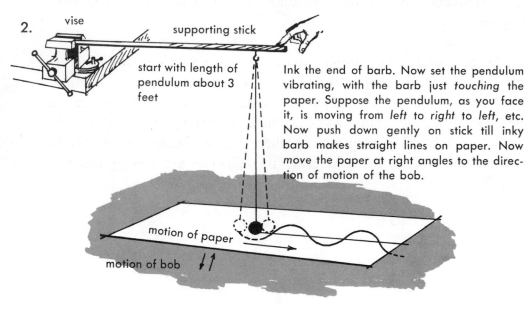

vise

supporting stick

start with length of pendulum about 3 feet

motion of paper

motion of bob

Ink the end of barb. Now set the pendulum vibrating, with the barb just *touching* the paper. Suppose the pendulum, as you face it, is moving from *left* to *right* to *left*, etc. Now push down gently on stick till inky barb makes straight lines on paper. Now *move* the paper at right angles to the direction of motion of the bob.

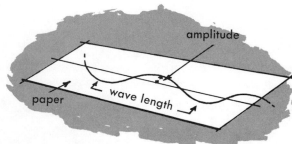

amplitude

paper

wave length

Do you see a curve on the paper? Try again. Move paper with steady speed. Raise bob only 1 or 2 inches from rest position to start it vibrating.

How long is your wave? It is the distance from *crest* to *crest* or from *trough* to *trough* of your trace. The amplitude is the maximum displacement of the bob from its position of rest.

Now *shorten* the length of your pendulum. Set it into vibration. Does it seem to swing faster — i.e., more back-and-forth movements per second?

3.

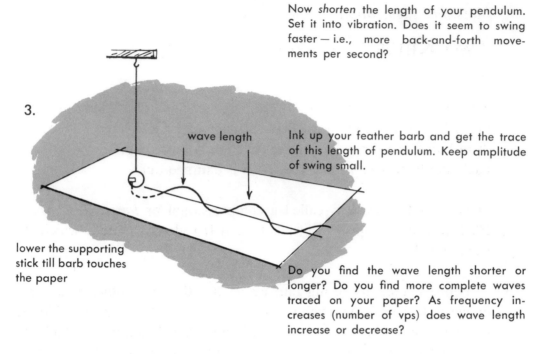

wave length

Ink up your feather barb and get the trace of this length of pendulum. Keep amplitude of swing small.

lower the supporting stick till barb touches the paper

Do you find the wave length shorter or longer? Do you find more complete waves traced on your paper? As frequency increases (number of vps) does wave length increase or decrease?

4.

Lower supporting stick till barb touches the paper.

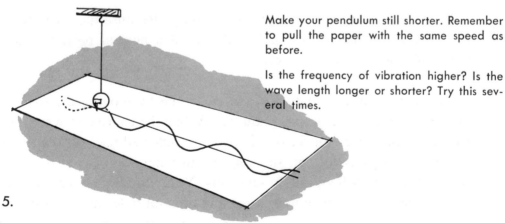

Make your pendulum still shorter. Remember to pull the paper with the same speed as before.

Is the frequency of vibration higher? Is the wave length longer or shorter? Try this several times.

5.

Try your own experiments. Vary the amplitude by making the pendulum swing through large and small arcs. What is the effect on the wave form or trace?

facts and ideas about . . .

Two Kinds of Waves

You are going to produce a *compression wave* in a taut spring by pressing a few of the coils together and then letting go. You will see the disturbance traveling along the spring. The compression will be reflected back and forth several times before it is damped out.

This kind of wave is called a compressional or *longitudinal wave*. Each turn of the spring vibrates to and fro along the path which the wave travels.

You will pull the spring taut again and this time *pluck* it at *right angles* to its length. You will see a wave that travels along the spring to the fixed end, where it is reflected. Notice the direction in which the coils and the particles in the coils, are moving. This kind of wave is called a *transverse wave* because the particles vibrate, or move to and fro, at *right angles* to the path along which the wave travels.

Sound waves are *longitudinal waves*. Why? Because the air particles in sound waves move back and forth, about a neutral position, along the path which the wave travels.

You will produce *standing waves* in a rope by moving the free end up and down with the proper frequency. When the transverse waves sent along the rope reach the fixed end, they are reflected back. If the timing of the vibrations is correct, *standing* or stationary waves are set up — that is, the rope will vibrate in segments. You will see permanently still points called *nodes,* and points of maximum amplitude called *anti-nodes.*

Standing waves are very common. As examples we have the vibrations of a tuning fork, the swaying of tall buildings, the vibrations of air columns in wind instruments, etc. Standing waves may be produced with either transverse or longitudinal waves.

You will also investigate water waves, using a basin of water and a small piece of cork. Study the motion of the bit of cork as waves pass over the surface of the water.

The motion of the cork will reveal how the particles of water move when a disturbance of waves pass. Does the cork move up and down? Then the particles of water which make up the wave must also move up and down. In other words, the particles of water move *transversely* or at *right angles* to the direction of the wave.

But water waves are not entirely transverse. If you watch carefully, you will see the cork move slightly back and forth as well as up and down. The water particles actually move in small circles or ellipses. Therefore water waves are both longitudinal and transverse.

Why are sound waves, which are longitudinal, usually diagramed as if they were transverse waves? Because it is convenient to represent sound and other longitudinal waves as if they were transverse waves. Keep in mind that the *amplitude* of the diagram represents the displacement of the air particles from rest positions in the case of a sound wave; and the *wave length* of the diagram represents the distance from one condensation to the next of a sound wave. Think about this.

Two Kinds of Waves

1. Longitudinal waves:

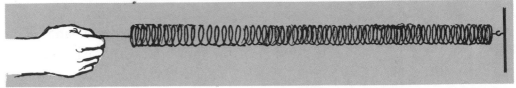

DO THIS: Obtain a wire spring, 2 to 3 feet long, at your local hardware store. Attach one end to a hook in wall or in a board. Pull spring taut. Now *compress* a small portion of the spring with other hand. Let go of the compressed portion suddenly. You will see a compression wave, or longitudinal wave, travel along the spring. Does the wave travel along the spring in the *same* direction as the coils vibrate? Explain.

2. Transverse waves:

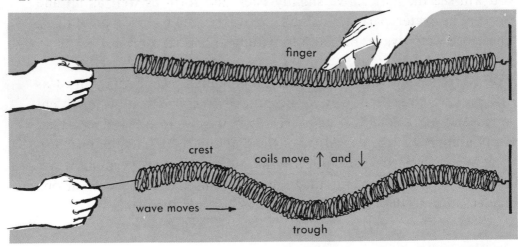

finger

crest

coils move ↑ and ↓

wave moves ⟶

trough

With your finger push *down* on the taut spring at right angles to its length. Let it up suddenly. Do you see a wave travel *along* the spring to the wall, where it reflected back again? Are the individual coils moving up and down *perpendicular* to the line of motion of the wave? Why do we call this type of wave a *transverse* wave? Try plucking the taut spring at different points — i.e., 1/4, 1/3, 1/2 of its length.

3. Transverse waves:

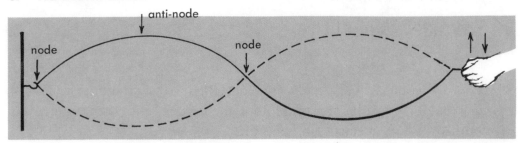

Attach a rope 6 to 9 feet long to the hook. Hold it taut at first. Now move hand up and down with a steady speed after moving forward slightly. Do you see a train of waves in the rope? If your hand moves up and down with the right frequency, you will see the rope divide into 2 or 3 sections. Waves reflected from the fixed end will have the same wave length and amplitude as the waves traveling towards the fixed end. This results in *standing waves*.

4. Water waves:

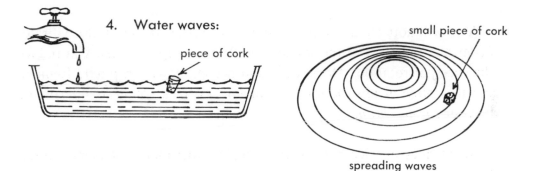

spreading waves

Float a small piece of cork on the water in a basin or pan. Let drops of water from faucet produce waves. Watch the movement of the cork. Does the cork move *with* the waves or rather up and down? Does the cork, borne up by the water particles, also move slightly forward, down, and back? As a wave moves to the right do the water particles, as shown by the cork, also move to the right? Is a water wave *longitudinal, transverse,* or both?

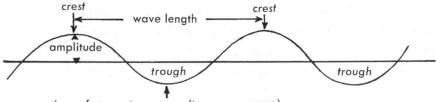

cross-section of a water wave (transverse wave)

Savart's Wheel

You are going to cut evenly spaced teeth on the circumference of a disk made of cardboard or of thin aluminum, and then rotate this toothed disk by means of a hand drill.

While rotating the disk, hold either a small card or a funnel-shaped piece of paper lightly against the teeth. You will hear a note produced by the impacts of the teeth against the card. The vibrations of the card will set up corresponding disturbances or vibrations in the surrounding air. Why?

You will notice that as the wheel rotates faster, the card also vibrates faster and the pitch of the sound rises. What happens when you reduce the speed of rotation? Does the sound become lower in pitch? Remember that *pitch* means the *highness* or *lowness* of a sound as interpreted by your *ear and brain.*

What does one learn from this simple experiment? It demonstrates that pitch depends on frequency of vibration, that is, on the number of vibrations per second. Or better, pitch depends on the number of pulses that strike the ear per second. Think about this: the higher the frequency, the higher the pitch; the lower the frequency, the lower the pitch.

Although musical instruments had been played for many centuries, it was Galileo (1564-1642) who seems to have been the first to observe the relationship between frequency and pitch. He passed a knife blade over the milled edge of a coin. He observed that this produced a musical sound that rose in pitch as the speed with which he moved the knife blade over the serrations increased. Try it with a coin. Also try moving the edge of a card across the teeth of a pocket comb at varying speeds.

The toothed disk you will make is called Savart's wheel after Félix Savart (1791-1841), a French physicist and surgeon.

If you know exactly how fast your disk turns, it is possible to calculate the frequency of the emitted note. Suppose your disk makes 120 revolutions per minute or 2 revolutions per second. If there are 48 teeth on the circumference of the disk, the frequency of the note must be 96 vps. Why?

A low bass voice can produce a note whose frequency is about 60 vps. High C, sometimes reached by soprano voices, has a frequency of 1036.

Would you call the sound produced by your toothed wheel a musical note? One important difference between a *musical sound* and a noise is that the former has a *definite* pitch. In other words, the brain interprets the stimuli reaching it from the ear as musical if the sound impulses arrive at *regular* intervals.

If its frequencies are irregular, we interpret the sound as a *noise*. Try making another toothed disk, this time with 48 *irregularly* spaced teeth. What kind of sound do you hear when this disk is rotated with a card held against the teeth? Explain.

Savart's Wheel

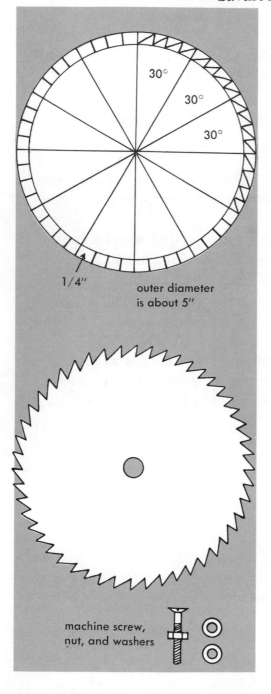

1/4"

outer diameter
is about 5"

machine screw,
nut, and washers

1. Make a toothed wheel.

DO THIS: Cut a circle about 5 inches in
diameter of stiff cardboard. With your compass draw another circle about 1/4 inch
from edge.

By means of a protractor divide the circle
into 12 parts or sectors, each 30 degrees.
Now divide each sector into 4 equal parts
by drawing short lines as shown. Draw short
diagonals and you will have an outline for
48 teeth. Cut teeth carefully.

Your toothed wheel will look
like this. Enlarge the hole in
its center.

Use machine screw, washers,
and nut to hold your cardboard disk firmly in hand drill.

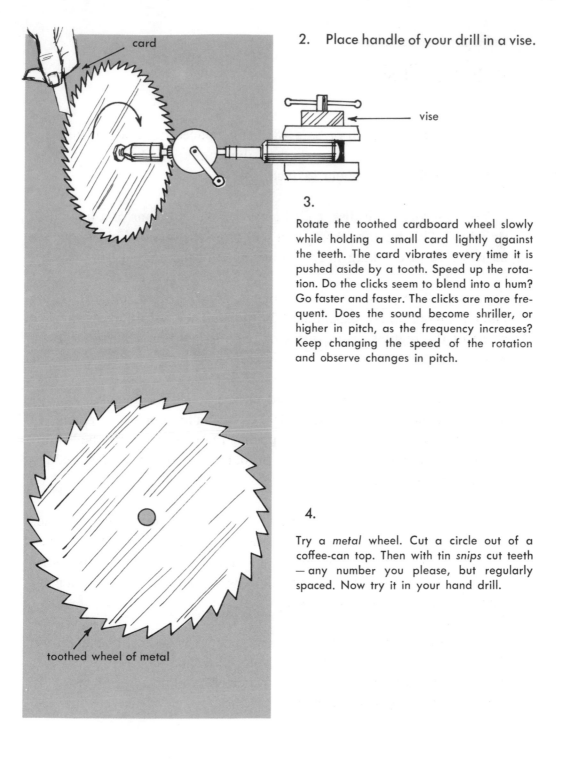

card

toothed wheel of metal

2. Place handle of your drill in a vise.

vise

3.

Rotate the toothed cardboard wheel slowly while holding a small card lightly against the teeth. The card vibrates every time it is pushed aside by a tooth. Speed up the rotation. Do the clicks seem to blend into a hum? Go faster and faster. The clicks are more frequent. Does the sound become shriller, or higher in pitch, as the frequency increases? Keep changing the speed of the rotation and observe changes in pitch.

4.

Try a *metal* wheel. Cut a circle out of a coffee-can top. Then with tin *snips* cut teeth — any number you please, but regularly spaced. Now try it in your hand drill.

facts and ideas about . . .

A Siren Disk

You are going to punch or bore 48 evenly spaced holes along the edge of a large disk made of cardboard or aluminum. The holes must all be of the *same* diameter, about ¼ inch.

You will rotate this disk, called a *siren* disk, by means of a hand drill as before. This time, however, you will blow a stream of air through a narrow tube or drinking straw through each of the holes as it passes by.

As each hole passes the stream of air, a puff goes through it. These puffs of air set up corresponding vibrations in the surrounding air. The result of the regular disturbances of the surrounding air is a series of waves or pulses.

You will try increasing the speed of rotation while blowing *steadily* through the holes in the moving disk. Does the note or sound change in pitch? Try slowing down. What happens? Do you recognize the "siren" sound even though your hand drill probably doesn't rotate fast enough to emit a piercing note?

The frequency of the note produced by your homemade *siren* depends on the number of holes in your disk and on the speed of rotation — i.e., revolutions per second. Once again, the higher the frequency, the higher the pitch; the lower the frequency, the lower the pitch. Is this statement true? Test it with your siren disk.

Try boring or punching another circle of holes a short distance from the outer circle of holes. This time you will space the holes *irregularly* or at varying distances from each other. But remember to make 48 holes, each of the same diameter, or about ¼ inch. Rotate the disk again. What kind of sounds do you get from the circle of unevenly spaced holes — noises or musical notes? Why?

Crova's disk is worth spending time making, for it "pictures" what takes place in air when trains of sound waves are set up by a vibrating body. Follow the directions on the next page. Notice that all circles, except the innermost one, are drawn with the compass needle on one of the eight equidistant points on the inner circle.

You will rotate Crova's disk slowly by means of a straw as explained. Do you see the waves radiating from the center? This interesting disk will help you visualize the state of the air when a train of sound waves passes through it. When rotated, the disk shows the movement of the layers or shells of air within the expanding spherical waves; the layers consist of particles of air moving closer together in regions of *condensations* and moving farther apart in regions of *rarefactions*.

Important facts: How fast does the disturbance created by a vibrating body move through the air? The speed of sound in air at 0° Centigrade is 1087 feet per second or 331 meters per second or 740 miles per hour. The speed of sound *increases* 2 feet per second, or 60 centimeters per second, for each centigrade degree above 0°C. The corresponding increase for each Fahrenheit degree above 32°F is 1.1 feet per second.

The Siren Disk

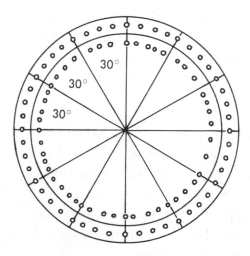

cardboard or aluminum disk about 12" in diameter (try aluminum pie plate)

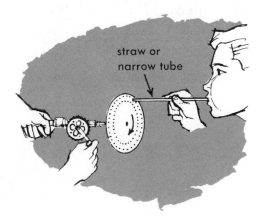

straw or narrow tube

1.

DO THIS: Cut a circle 12 inches in diameter out of cardboard or thin aluminum. Divide as shown into twelve 30-degree sectors, using a protractor to do this. Now mark off 48 equidistant points near the edge of your disk. Then with an awl or sharp nail pierce disk at these points to make 48 equidistant 1/4-inch holes. Below this outer circle drawn another circle. Now pierce disk again to make 48 unevenly spaced 1/4-inch holes.

2.

Fasten disk in hand drill using a machine screw, nut, and washers as before. Rotate disk in hand drill.

Blow stream of air through holes as disk rotates. Try speeding disk up and then slowing it down. Do you get a musical note from the outer ring of holes? What effect on the pitch, or shrillness, of the sound does more rapid rotation have?

Try same with *irregularly* spaced holes. Is the sound musical, or merely a *noise*?

3.

Try piercing disk to form a third circle — this time with only 24 equidistant 1/4-inch holes. Be sure to push awl *same distance* through disk to make the holes exactly the same diameter. Compare tone of note from 24-hole circle with note from 48-hole circle.

4-millimeter divisions

Crova's Disk

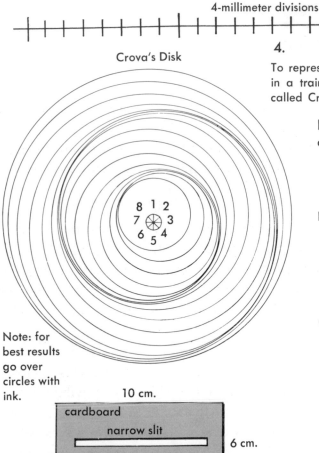

```
      8 1 2
      7 ⊛ 3
      6 5 4
```

Note: for
best results
go over
circles with
ink.

10 cm.

cardboard

narrow slit

6 cm.

look through slit at spinning disk

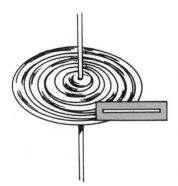

4.

To represent the motion of the layers of air in a train of sound waves, make a device called Crova's disk.

DO THIS:
a) Use a large card. Draw a circle near middle of card with a radius of 4 millimeters. Divide this circle into 8 equal and numbered parts as shown.
b) Place compass point on No. 1 mark of inner circle and draw a circle with a radius of 20 millimeters (2 centimeters).
c) Place compass point on No. 2 mark of inner circle and draw a circle 24 millimeters in radius.
d) Place compass point on No. 3 mark of inner circle and draw circle 28 millimeters in radius.
e) Continue around the inner circle, making the radius of each circle 4 millimeters longer than the one before. You will thus draw 8 eccentric circles.
f) Continue round the inner circle a second time, again making the radius of each circle 4 millimeters longer in radius than the one before. This will result in a total of 16 eccentric circles.

Use your Crova's Disk as follows:
a) Bore hole in center the width of a drinking straw. Insert straw and spin disk. Or use a hand drill to rotate the disk.
b) Do you see waves as disk rotates? Do the waves seem to crowd together, move apart, draw together, and then separate again?
c) Use your disk. Try experiments of your own. Vary speed. View the disk without the viewing slit and then with it.

facts and ideas about . . .

The Doppler Effect

You are going to investigate the change in pitch of a sound proceeding from an approaching or receding source. This phenomenon is called the Doppler effect after the Austrian physicist, Christian Doppler (1803-1853), who was the first to work out a satisfactory explanation of it.

In your experiment you will have someone whirl a whistle about his head while blowing it through a long rubber tube. As the whistle moves on its circular path you will listen to it carefully from a position a few feet away. Notice that at one moment the revolving whistle is moving towards you, the observer; and at another moment the whistle is moving away from you.

Why do you detect a regular rise and fall in pitch as the whistle moves in its circle? The source of sound, that is, the whistle, is moving towards the observer in one part of its path at the same time as it is emitting sound waves. This results in the crowding up of the sound waves. Why? This crowding decreases the distance between successive wave crests, that is, it decreases the wave lengths of the train of sound waves. A greater number of waves therefore reach the observer's ears each second. This is another way of saying that the frequency increases and the pitch rises. Think about this.

Suppose the whirling whistle happens to be on the part of its path where it is moving away from you. The whistle now draws away from the waves it is sending backwards. The successive waves thus spread over a longer distance than when the whistle is at rest. The distance between successive wave crests becomes longer — i.e., the wave length increases. A small number of waves therefore reach the observer's ears each second. This means that the frequency decreases and the apparent pitch falls.

Keep this in mind about the Doppler effect: While the source of sound is moving *towards* the observer, he hears a note higher in pitch than when both he and the source were stationary. And when the source of sound is moving *away from* him, the observer hears a note lower in pitch than when the source and he were stationary. *No change* in pitch will be heard in either of the above cases. A *change* can only be *heard* when the motion changes from approach to recession, or from recession to approach. Can you explain why?

Interesting facts about the Doppler effect:

(a) When a whistling locomotive rushes past an observer standing on a railroad station platform, he notices that the pitch of the whistle is higher as the train approaches than as it recedes. Also a fast-moving car with horn blowing will seem to emit a sound of higher pitch while approaching an observer standing at the side of the road than after it has passed him. Can you explain these two cases?

(b) The pitch also undergoes an apparent change when the *source of sound* is stationary, as in the case of a clanging bell at a railroad crossing when the *observer* is in motion on a moving train. Try to work out the rise and fall in pitch for this example by applying Doppler's principle.

(c) Doppler's principle has been used in astronomy to determine whether a star is moving towards or away from the earth. A star moving towards the earth emits light waves, each particular wave length of which is slightly shorter than the wave length of corresponding light from a stationary source on the earth's surface. Hence the star's spectrum will show a shift or displacement towards the violet end of the spectrum. For similar reasons a star moving away from the earth will show a shift towards the red end of the spectrum. Note that the longer waves of the spectrum are near the red end and the shorter waves near the violet end.

Doppler Effect

1. You will need:

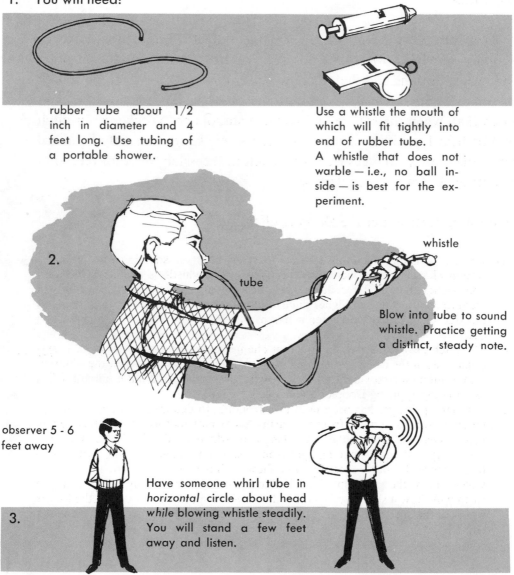

rubber tube about 1/2 inch in diameter and 4 feet long. Use tubing of a portable shower.

Use a whistle the mouth of which will fit tightly into end of rubber tube.
A whistle that does not warble — i.e., no ball inside — is best for the experiment.

whistle

tube

2.

Blow into tube to sound whistle. Practice getting a distinct, steady note.

observer 5 - 6 feet away

3. Have someone whirl tube in *horizontal* circle about head *while* blowing whistle steadily. You will stand a few feet away and listen.

The vibrating whistle moves *towards* the observer in one part of its path, and away from the observer in another part of its path. Do you detect a *change* in the pitch of the sound as the whistle changes from an *approaching* motion to a *receding* motion? When does the sound seem higher? Lower? Why?

4.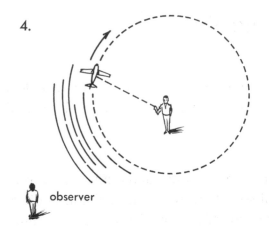

If possible, listen to the sound emitted by the miniature gas-engine of a powered model airplane moving in a circle. Do you detect a change in pitch as the airplane changes from approach to recession in relation to you? Explain.

observer

5.  bell with clapper  observer

TRY THIS: Have a friend keep ringing a bell as he rides his bicycle rapidly towards you and past you. Do you notice a change in pitch of the bell as it passes you? Explain.

6. 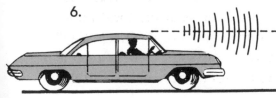 observer

Station yourself near a road where automobiles travel 40 to 60 miles per hour. Does the sound made by tires change in pitch as the cars pass you? Why? Does the sound of a blowing horn on a moving car change in pitch as the car passes you? Why? Check the changing pitch of the gong on a fire truck under similar conditions.

facts and ideas about . . .

The Reflection of Sound Waves

For this experiment you will use a homemade curved mirror to reflect sound waves. A ticking wrist watch will be the source of the sound waves.

You will find the focus or focal point of your curved mirror. Keep in mind that the laws of reflection of sound are the same as the laws of reflection of light. A curved surface will reflect sound waves in a manner similar to that in which a curved mirror reflects light.

You will place the ticking wrist watch at the focus of your curved mirror. "Beams" of sound will then be reflected parallel to the principal axis of the mirror. Is this what happened with light beams, too? Try placing the watch inside the focus, at the focus, and outside the focus. In which position is the ticking sound most distinct? Why?

You will find the distance at which the ticking sound is barely audible when there is no curved reflector or mirror behind it. Now place your curved mirror behind the watch, so that the latter is at the focal point. Does the sound of the ticking become louder or more distinct? Why? Move away from the watch. How far away can your ear be, with the curved reflector in proper position, before the sound becomes inaudible? Try it.

Repeat the experiment, using a curved soup bowl as a reflector. Find the focal point of the curved bowl by moving the watch closer or further away from the center of the bowl. The point where the ticking sounds loudest to you may be regarded as the focal point. Why?

Echoes are produced by the reflection of sound. The reflector of sound may be a building, a wall, a cliff, a clump of trees, and so on. The roll of thunder is the result of successive reflections of the original sound by different cloud masses.

To hear an echo, the reflected sound must reach your ear *more* than one-tenth of a second after the original sound. You will then hear two separate sounds, the original and the reflected sound.

Remember that the effect of any sound on your ear lasts for about one-tenth of a second after the sound waves have stopped striking it. Therefore, if the reflected sound reaches your ear quickly, or in *less* than one-tenth of a second after the original sound, the two sounds blend. In other words, you hear not two sounds but rather one prolonged sound.

In small rooms sound is reflected from ceilings, floors, walls, etc. But you do not hear echoes. Why? You hear single sounds which are a blend of the original and reflected sounds. The reflection of sound in this case often produces *reverberations*, which differ from echoes in that there is no distinct repetition but only the persistence or prolongation of the original sound.

Echoes present a problem in large rooms. Reflected waves return more than one-tenth of a second after the original waves; and as a result two separate sounds are heard. Sound-absorbing wall coverings and hangings are sometimes used to reduce the reflection of sound from these surfaces. How far away must a reflecting surface be before it can produce an echo by a single reflection? In one-tenth of a second sound will travel 113 feet at normal room temperature. Therefore, the reflecting surface must be more than half this distance from the sound source — i.e., more than 56.5 feet. Explain.

33

Reflection of Sound

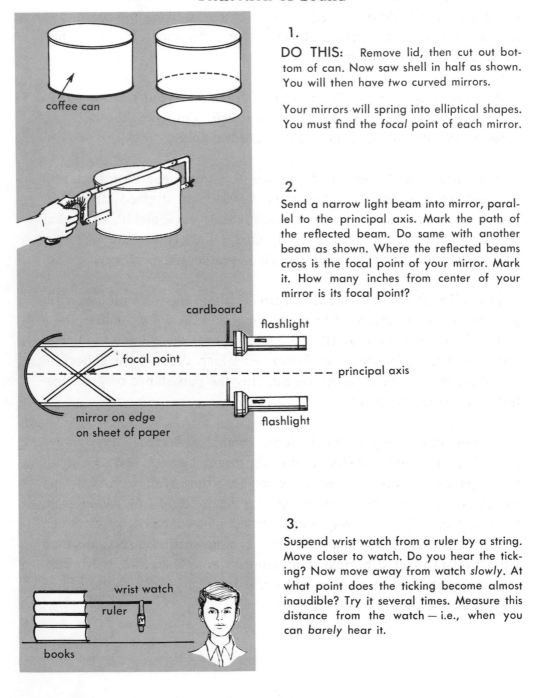

coffee can

cardboard

flashlight

focal point

principal axis

mirror on edge
on sheet of paper

flashlight

wrist watch

ruler

books

1.

DO THIS: Remove lid, then cut out bottom of can. Now saw shell in half as shown. You will then have *two* curved mirrors.

Your mirrors will spring into elliptical shapes. You must find the *focal* point of each mirror.

2.

Send a narrow light beam into mirror, parallel to the principal axis. Mark the path of the reflected beam. Do same with another beam as shown. Where the reflected beams cross is the focal point of your mirror. Mark it. How many inches from center of your mirror is its focal point?

3.

Suspend wrist watch from a ruler by a string. Move closer to watch. Do you hear the ticking? Now move away from watch *slowly*. At what point does the ticking become almost inaudible? Try it several times. Measure this distance from the watch — i.e., when you can *barely* hear it.

4.

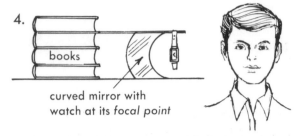

curved mirror with
watch at its *focal point*

If focal point is 1 inch from mirror, place
mirror so that its center is 1 inch from watch.
If focal point is 2 inches from the center of
mirror, place mirror 2 inches from watch, etc.
Place your ear at the distance at which the
ticking was inaudible before. Can you hear
the ticking when mirror is present? Does the
mirror *reflect* sound waves?

5. EXPLANATION:

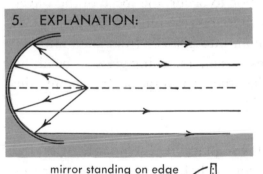

The laws of reflection of sound are the same
as the laws of reflection of light. Most of the
sound waves originating at the *focal point*
strike the mirror surface and are then reflected as a *parallel* beam.

mirror standing on edge

curved
mirror

6. TRY THIS:

Move mirror so that watch is *less* than focal
distance from center of mirror. Is the sound
more or less distinct? Try making the distance of the watch *greater* than the focal
length of the mirror.

7. TRY THIS:

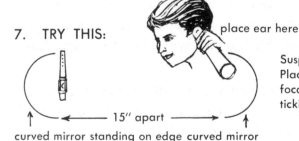

place ear here

Suspend watch at focal point of one mirror.
Place ear trumpet of rolled up paper at
focal point of other mirror. Do you hear the
ticking? Explain.

← 15″ apart →

curved mirror standing on edge curved mirror

facts and ideas about . . .

Refraction of Sound

You are going to place a toy balloon filled with air in the path of sound waves. Will the air in the balloon act like a lens and produce refraction or bending of the sound waves passing through it? Try it. You will repeat the experiment, this time using a balloon that you have blown up with air from your lungs. Finally, you will try a balloon filled with carbon dioxide, which is easily prepared.

The bending of waves on passing from one medium to another is called *refraction*. In order for refraction to occur, the speed of the waves in the two mediums or substances must be different. Light waves, for example, bend when they pass from air into glass or from glass into air. The curved surfaces of a convex lens — i.e., a burning glass — bend the light rays passing through it so that they converge at one point, the "burning" spot. Can you explain why?

Since the refraction of sound takes place in accordance with the same laws that apply to the refraction of light, a lens in the shape of your balloon and filled with carbon dioxide should converge the sound waves passing through it. Why? Sound travels with a speed of 1087 feet per second in air at 0° C. Sound travels with a speed of only 846 feet per second in carbon dioxide at 0°C. Will a beam of sound bend as it passes from air into carbon dioxide? From carbon dioxide into air? Will the carbon dioxide balloon act like a convex lens and converge the sound to a point or focus? Your experiments will answer this question.

Before using the balloons to find out which will act like a lens, suspend a wrist watch by a string and then move away from it slowly until the ticking sound just becomes inaudible. You will then proceed to move the balloons, one at a time, between the watch and your ear, without changing your own distance from the watch.

Does the sound of the ticking become audible when the air-filled balloon is between your ear and the watch? You will then try the balloon filled with exhaled air, which contains about 4 per cent carbon dioxide. Finally try the one filled with carbon dioxide. In each case you will move the *balloon*, but not the watch or your head, as explained on the next page.

Additional facts about the refraction of sound:

(a) The most common experience with refraction is one produced when sound travels through layers of air that are at different temperatures. Remember that the speed of sound is greater in warm air than in cold air. The speed of sound increases by 2 feet per second for every degree Centigrade rise in temperature above $0°C$.
(b) Suppose there is a layer of cold air close to the ground and a warmer layer above it. This condition often exists on a lake in the early morning while the water is still cold. Voices, music, shouts, and so forth seem to carry greater distances at such times than later in the day when the sun is high. Why? Because the sound waves are always bent or refracted *away* from the substance in which they travel faster. In this case the greater speed is in the warm upper layer of air. The sound waves are therefore bent *downward* when they strike the warm upper layer and thus move close to the water.
(c) After the sun has warmed the water, the air next to the water becomes warmer than the air above it. The sound of voices, music, and so forth does not carry as far now as in the early morning. Why? The faster medium or substance is now the layer next to the water, since this layer is warmer than the air above it. The sound waves now bend *away* from this faster or warmer layer. Hence the sound is refracted upward. Do you see why sounds do not carry far under these conditions?
(d) Here is a more common case of the refraction of sound: At night the air next to the ground is often cooler than air higher up. Sound waves travel faster along the ground at night than in the daytime. Can you explain why?

Refraction of Sound

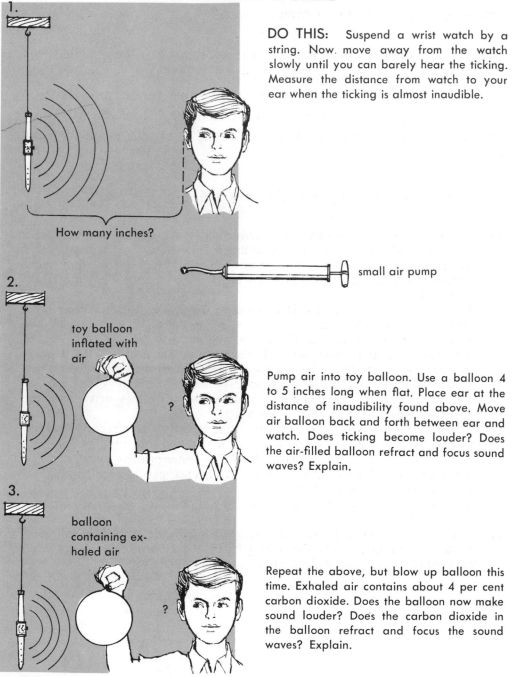

DO THIS: Suspend a wrist watch by a string. Now move away from the watch slowly until you can barely hear the ticking. Measure the distance from watch to your ear when the ticking is almost inaudible.

1.

How many inches?

small air pump

2.

toy balloon inflated with air

Pump air into toy balloon. Use a balloon 4 to 5 inches long when flat. Place ear at the distance of inaudibility found above. Move air balloon back and forth between ear and watch. Does ticking become louder? Does the air-filled balloon refract and focus sound waves? Explain.

3.

balloon containing exhaled air

Repeat the above, but blow up balloon this time. Exhaled air contains about 4 per cent carbon dioxide. Does the balloon now make sound louder? Does the carbon dioxide in the balloon refract and focus the sound waves? Explain.

4. You will prepare carbon dioxide by doing the following:

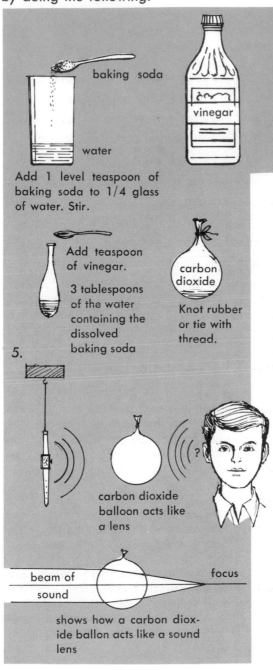

baking soda

vinegar

water

Large toy balloon about 4 - 5 inches long when flat

Add 1 level teaspoon of baking soda to 1/4 glass of water. Stir.

Add teaspoon of vinegar.

3 tablespoons of the water containing the dissolved baking soda

carbon dioxide

Knot rubber or tie with thread.

Caution: If balloon fills too quickly, *release neck* and let gas escape. Try again, using less vinegar.

The balloon should round out as it fills with carbon dioxide. If insufficient gas is produced, start again, but this time use 2 teaspoons of vinegar. *Don't over-inflate.* A rounded balloon as big as a baseball will do.

5.

carbon dioxide balloon acts like a lens

beam of sound

focus

shows how a carbon dioxide ballon acts like a sound lens

Move the balloon back and forth as before. Do you hear the ticking distinctly now? Is the sound bent or refracted by the carbon dioxide? Explain. Also try moving farther from the watch. Does the balloon help you hear the ticking at the new distance? Explain.

facts and ideas about . . .

Diffraction of Sound

You are going to investigate the bending of sound waves once again. This time, however, we'll observe the bending that usually takes place when waves meet obstacles, or when waves spread out after passing through a narrow aperture or slit. Diffraction is a phenomenon that occurs in water waves and light waves as well as in sound waves.

In your experiments you will use a transparent tank, perhaps a shoe box made of clear plastic, containing about an inch of water. You will set up waves in the water as explained on the next page. A light under the tank will throw the image of the waves on the ceiling so that you will be able to detect changes in direction of the waves when these occur. Remember that what you learn about water waves is also true of sound waves.

First let us list a few common experiences with diffraction:

(a) At the seashore you often see waves sweeping around piers or around rocks jutting from the water. The waves are usually long, that is, the distance between successive crests may be hundreds of times longer than the width of the obstacle. On meeting the pier, for example, such waves divide, bend or pass around it, and immediately reunite on the other side. This is an example of diffraction. Why?

(b) Suppose the waves are short, or mere ripples. Their wave lengths are now small compared with the width of the obstacle or pier. The ripples strike the pier and are reflected *back*, spreading out in all directions. A "shadow" forms on the other side of the obstacle. Why? In this case there is very little bending or diffraction.

(c) Sound waves behave in a similar manner. When long waves, that is, waves such as are emitted by brass instruments, meet an obstacle much smaller than the wave lengths of the sounds, the waves bend around the obstacle readily. You can hear the low notes of a brass band that is still around the corner and out of sight. Why? Because the low-pitched notes of long wave length bend around the edges of obstacles with little loss of intensity.

40

(d) Suppose the brass band suddenly turns the corner and you can see it. You have been hearing the low notes with long wave lengths. Now you can hear the higher-pitched notes with shorter wave lengths, most of which had not reached your ears while the band was out of sight. Why? Think of the water ripples and the pier. Short waves do not bend around the edges of obstacles, or around corners, as readily as long waves.

In your experiments with the transparent tank you will place first a narrow and then a wide obstacle in the path of a plane or flat water wave. Do the waves manage to pass around a narrow obstacle? A wide obstacle? In which case are the waves reflected back, thus forming a "shadow" behind the obstacle? Try it. See if you can explain your results.

Then try passing a water wave first through a narrow slit and then through a wide slit, as explained on the next page. Does a flat wave become curved after passing through a narrow slit? Try it. If the answer is yes, then the wave spreading circularly from the slit has undergone diffraction. Why? Then try the wider slit to see if a flat wave remains flat or almost flat after passing through the slit.

It is important to keep in mind that "wide" and "narrow" are used in comparison with the wave lengths of the incoming waves in your tank. This means the distance from the crest of one water wave to the crest of the next wave. A wide slit is one that is larger than the wave lengths of your waves; a narrow slit is one that is smaller than the wave length of your water waves. Think about this. Try variations of this experiment on your own.

One more example of diffraction: Suppose a radio is playing outdoors. Will the sound waves pass through an open window and spread to all parts of a room? Here the window is the aperture, which is small compared with most of the wave lengths emitted by the radio. Will the waves spread circularly, that is, bend around the window frame? Explain.

41

Diffraction of Sound Waves

1. You will need:

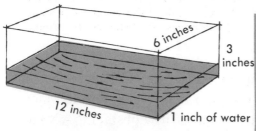

6 inches

3 inches

12 inches

1 inch of water

Any tank, glass, or plastic of at least the above dimensions will do. Clear plastic shoeboxes are sold at ten-cent stores.

Also

stick about 1/4 inch wide

6 1/4"

stick about 2 inches wide

2 1/2"

cardboard screen with 1/8-inch slit

2 1/2"

cardboard screen with 2-inch slit or aperture

2. Arrange as shown

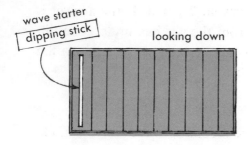

wave starter

dipping stick

looking down

DO THIS: Dip stick horizontally into water. Are flat, that is, plane waves, produced? Stick must be in position shown in diagram. Observe image of waves on ceiling when there is an electric light bulb under box as shown below.

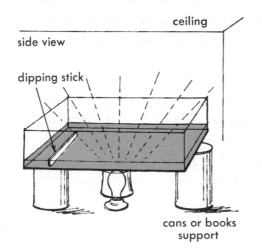

ceiling

side view

dipping stick

cans or books support

Look at ceiling while stirring up waves. Move box or cans or bulb until you see wave images on ceiling most distinctly. *Practice!* Try a shade around bulb and see if it improves distinctness of wave images on ceiling.

Waves meet narrow and wide obstacles.
Light bulb is under tank.

wide stick
upright in tank

3.

(tank, looking down)

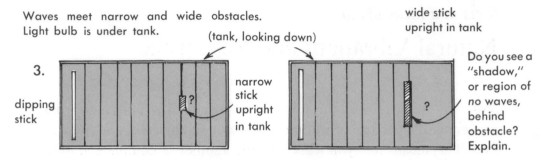

dipping
stick

narrow
stick
upright
in tank

Do you see a
"shadow,"
or region of
no waves,
behind
obstacle?
Explain.

Narrow obstacle in path of waves. Look at ceiling. Do flat waves appear on other side of obstacle? Have waves bent around obstacle?

Wide obstacle in path of waves. Look at ceiling. Do you see a full wave behind obstacle? Is there a "shadow" behind the wide obstacle? Explain.

4.

Waves passing through a narrow aperture.
Light bulb is under tank.

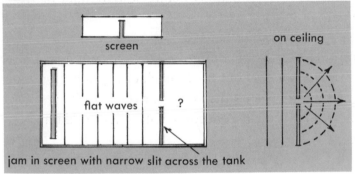

screen

on ceiling

flat waves   ?

jam in screen with narrow slit across the tank

Do you see circular
waves in ceiling on
other side of slit? If so,
waves have undergone
diffraction? They are
now moving in new
directions. See arrows.
Explain.

5.

Waves passing through a wide aperture.
Light bulb is under tank.

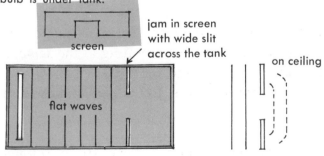

screen

jam in screen
with wide slit
across the tank

on ceiling

flat waves

Do you see flat, or
nearly flat waves on
ceiling on other side of
wide slit? Is there only
a small amount of
bending or diffraction?
Why?

6.

Try various obstacles and slits on your own.

facts and ideas about . . .

Natural Vibrations and Resonance

You are going to find the natural frequency of a particular rocking chair and of a particular pendulum when these objects are set into vibration. This means that you will count the number of complete vibrations, or *over-and-back* movements, per minute in each case.

Try to increase the natural frequency of the above vibrating bodies by applying a slight push at the right time — i.e., at the *instant* when a vibrating body *changes* the direction of vibration. In other words, you will push the rocking chair and the pendulum bob in *unison* with the natural vibrations of each. Will the force you apply change the number of vibrations per minute? Try it.

To get the rocking chair or the pendulum to start vibrating *you* have to move it from its original position of rest. In each case gravity provides the *restoring force* and inertia causes the body to overshoot its rest position. The back-and-forth movement continues until friction 'damps out' the motion. See page 9.

Now suspend four pendulums from a common support, as explained on the experiment page. You will start one pendulum swinging and then observe the behavior of the other pendulums.

Will the impulses transmitted through the common supporting cord cause one of the other pendulums to start vibrating at the *same natural frequency* as the pendulum you set into motion? Which of the three pendulums *responds* to the *driver,* that is, to the pendulum you set into vibration. Why?

Your experiment with the four pendulums demonstrates *resonance* of

44

a mechanical nature. In sound, we say that resonance or sympathetic vibration exists when an object is set into vibration at its own *natural frequency* by impulses from another object. Try singing near a piano with the loud pedal down. Will any of the piano strings be set into audible vibration? If one or more are, then the frequencies of some of the sound waves striking the strings must be equal to the natural frequencies of the responding strings. Why? Try it.

You will hold the openings of various bottles, tubes, shells, etc. next to your ear. Do you hear a hum with a particular note? Why? The air chamber within each bottle or shell acts as a *resonator* for sound waves of a particular wave length. Does the size and shape of the container change the natural frequency of the air within it? Try it.

What sets the air chambers listed above into sympathetic vibration? The air around you is full of sounds of different pitch made by various vibrating bodies. These sound waves, of mixed frequencies, dash against the open mouths of your bottles, etc. But to get the air chamber within a particular bottle or shell to vibrate energetically, the outside waves must have a frequency that corresponds to the natural frequency of the mass of air in the air chamber. Remember that the note you hear is produced by many small impulses arriving at the mouth of the container at the right intervals.

Helmholtz resonators, used to detect vibrations of a particular frequency, consist of spherical shells of different diameters. Each shell has two openings: one for outside sound waves to enter, and another where the ear is applied. These resonators are named after H. L. F. von Helmholtz (1821–1894), a German physicist.

Natural Vibrations and Resonance

1. Natural vibration.

Place a rocking chair on a hard surface. Start it rocking with a gentle push or pull. Count the number of complete vibrations — i.e., back and forth movements — in 10 or 15 seconds. Multiply by 6 or 4, respectively, to find the vibrations per *minute*. Do this several times. Average your results.

Now try it again. This time give rocker a *slight* push *each* time it starts moving *away* from you. Find vibration frequency. Average the results of several trials. How many vibrations per minute now? Suppose you found the frequency 40 vibrations per minute *without* your slight "extra" push. Did this "extra" push increase the frequency? Or did the frequency remain the same?

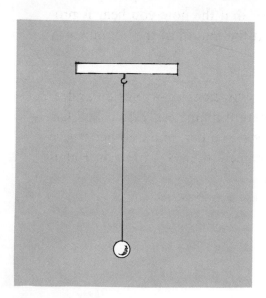

2.

Suspend a pendulum of any length you please — i.e., 1 to 3 feet. Set it vibrating over a small arc, that is, 2 or 3 inches from rest position. Find the number of *complete* vibrations in 15 seconds; in one minute.

Now repeat the above, but this time give pendulum bob a slight push *each* time it starts moving away from you. Once again find its frequency of vibration. Do the "extra pushes" *increase* the number of vibrations per minute? Explain.

3. Resonance.

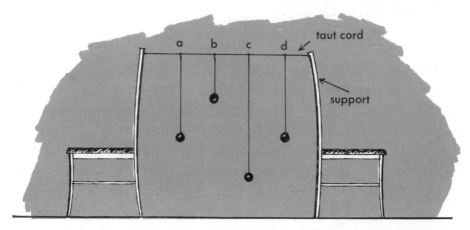

a   b   c   d   taut cord

support

Run taut cord between two supports — i.e., backs of chairs or wooden posts. Attach 4 pendulums, using bobs or any weights tied to strings. Make "a" and "d" the *same* length, perhaps 15 inches. Make "b" a few inches shorter than "a," and "c" a few inches longer than "a."

Start "a" swinging or oscillating through a short arc. Observe "b," "c," and "d" carefully. Which pendulum is most readily set swinging by the to-and-fro motion of "a"? Do the vibrations of "a," transmitted through the supporting cord, affect the other pendulums? Explain.

4.

Sympathetic vibrations or resonance:

Put variously shaped hollow containers — bottles, flasks, shells, etc. — up to your ear. Air within each vessel is set into vibration by sound waves reaching the mouth of the vessel from the *outside*. How does this resemble the mechanical resonance in Experiment 3 above? Are the sounds emitted by the various containers different in pitch? Why?

cardboard tube

Adjust size of opening with a card.

bottle   shell   drinking glasses

facts and ideas about . . .

Sounding Boards

You are going to strike the prongs of an ordinary fork against rubber or wood and note the loudness of the resulting sound. Strike the fork again, this time placing the base of the vibrating fork firmly against a door panel. Is the sound emitted by the fork louder now? Why? Are the vibrations of the door panel produced by resonance, as in the previous experiment? Or is the door panel forced to vibrate in unison with the fork, regardless of the natural frequency of the door panel? Explain.

When the fork is held in the hand and the prongs are vibrating, very little energy is passed on to the surrounding air. Why? Since the prongs are quite narrow, the nearby air instead of being pushed aside tends to flow around the moving prongs. For this reason the air some distance away is only slightly disturbed by the vibrating prongs. Do you see why the sound is weak or almost inaudible?

When the vibrating fork is pressed against the door panel, the latter is *forced* to vibrate in unison with the fork. As a result, the large mass of air next to the door panel is set into vibration too, and the loudness of the sound is multiplied many times. The door panel, in other words, acts as a sounding board. We call the vibrations set up in the panel *forced vibrations*. Why? Keep in mind that vibrations like those of your sounding board can be produced with any fork, large or small; that is, forced vibrations can be produced in the board by any fork, no matter what its frequency.

You will try a similar experiment with a fine wire stretched between two points, as in the diagram on the next page. Observe the loudness of the sound emitted when the wire is plucked. Is the volume of air set into vibration small? Explain. You will then mount the wire on a board, keeping the length the same and using two wooden bridges as shown in the diagrams. Will the board under the wire now act as a sounding board and make the sound louder? Why? Try this.

Are the bridges necessary? Yes, for they transmit the vibrations from the wire to the board. Your board will thus be *forced* to vibrate at the same frequency of the string or wire in contact with it. This takes place regardless of the board's natural frequency (see page 45), which depends on its size, weight, shape, etc. Inside a piano is a large sounding board that is set into vibration by the vibrations of the wires in contact with it. Do you see why a piano produces a fuller sound than a harp? Explain.

The body of a violin acts as a sounding board. The vibrations of the string are conveyed to the body or belly of the violin by the wooden bridge. Forced vibrations are thus set up not only in the thin wood but also in the air of the cavity in the violin body. The explanation of the characteristic tone produced by a violin is very complex. It involves, in addition to the forced vibrations of the wood and air chamber, the reinforcement of certain notes by the free or natural vibrations of the body of the violin.

You will attach a thin wire, using bridges as before, to the top of a wooden box, one end of which is open, as shown in the diagram on the next page. Is the sound produced by plucking louder now than when a simple board was used? Why? Is the box itself forced to vibrate at the frequency of the vibrating wire? Is the air in the box also forced to vibrate in unison with the wire? Try it. Do you think that the size of the air chamber in the box is important? Explain.

Sounding Boards

1. Forced vibrations.

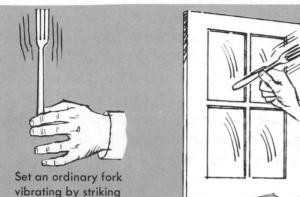

Set an ordinary fork vibrating by striking against rubber or wood, or by compressing and then suddenly releasing the prongs.

Try placing vibrating fork in contact with door panel as shown. Does sound become louder? Why? Is the door panel being *forced* to vibrate in unison with the fork? Try same with different-size forks.

door panel acting as a sounding board

2.

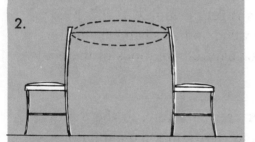

Tie a thin iron wire to chair backs as shown. Use #30 galvanized wire, called "flower wire." Move chairs to make wire taut. Pluck wire in middle, with thumbnail. Is the sound "full" or "thin"? Explain. Is the sound reinforced?

3. Effect of a sounding board.

Drive two nails into a board. Attach #30 wire to nails. Use wooden bridges under wire to convey vibrations to the board. Pluck taut wire with thumbnail. Wire should be same length as No. 2 above. Is sound fuller, louder, now that it is reinforced by the sounding board? Why?

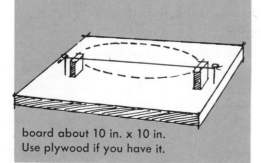

board about 10 in. x 10 in. Use plywood if you have it.

4. Using a sounding board and a vibrating chamber of air to reinforce sound.

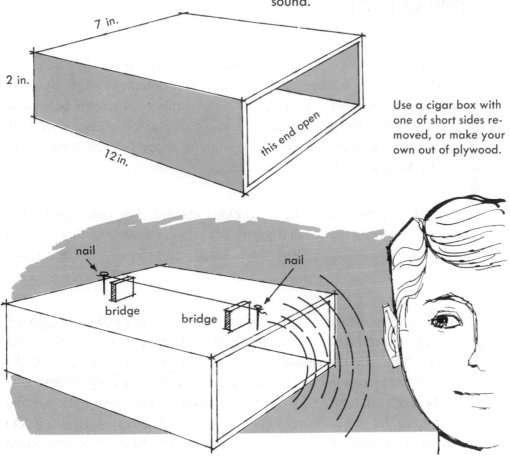

Use a cigar box with one of short sides removed, or make your own out of plywood.

Keep length of wire between bridges same as in Part 2 and 3. Be sure wire is taut. Pluck it in middle. Is sound louder than when a simple board was used as a sounding board. Why? Is the wooden part of the box forced to vibrate in unison with the vibrating wire? Is the air in the box also forced to vibrate in unison with the vibrating wire? Explain.

5. Try setting the base of your vibrating fork on the flat board and then on the box. Is there any difference in loudness? Why?

facts and ideas about . . .

Tone Quality

You are going to make a simple sonometer by stretching a thin wire over a board or a box, as explained in the diagram on the next page. You will pluck the stretched wire at different points along its length and listen carefully to the tones produced. Since you will pluck the same wire with the same force at different points you might expect all the tones to be identical. Are they? Try it.

Suppose you pluck the wire at its exact middle. The note you hear is mainly the *fundamental* of that particular string or wire. In this case the wire vibrates as a whole, or as a single loop, and produces its *lowest* possible note.

Now pluck the wire again, using the same force, at a point one-quarter of its length from one end. The wire will vibrate in two equal segments and as a whole, simultaneously. The two equal parts or segments of the wire are vibrating twice as fast as the same wire vibrating as a whole. The vibrating segments add the first overtone, also called the second harmonic, to the fundamental note that the whole string is emitting. Do you observe any difference in clarity of the combined tones as compared with the fundamental note sounded by itself? Try it several times on your stretched wire.

We say that the *quality* of the two tones you are comparing differs. The quality of a musical sound depends on the number and prominence of the overtones which are present. You can distinguish the sound of a violin from that of a piano or clarinet even though the sounds may be of the same pitch and loudness. You can recognize the voices of friends before the speakers come into sight. Why? Because the sounds reaching your ear in each of these cases consist of a different mixture of fundamental and overtones. In other words, they differ in quality.

The study of what are now called overtones began with the publication by Marin Mersenne (1588–1648), a French philosopher and mathematician, of the results of his investigation of the vibrations of strings. The major work on the quality of sounds, however, was done by Hermann von Helmholtz, the German physicist.

A few details about the experiments on the next page:

(a) You will once again pluck the stretched wire at the one-quarter point, but this time touch the middle of the vibrating wire lightly and quickly with the edge of a card. Does the sound cease or do you now hear a higher note? Try it several times. Note that touching the vibrating wire in the middle stopped the vibrations as a whole *without* interfering with the vibrations of the two segments. See diagram on next page.
(b) Suppose you sound the fundamental by plucking the wire at its mid-point. Now touch the middle of the vibrating wire lightly with the edge of the card. Does the sound cease entirely this time? Why?
(c) You will also make the wire vibrate in three equal parts and thus produce the second overtone, as explained on the experiment page. The addition of this overtone to the fundamental usually gives brilliance to the tone you hear because of the overtone's high pitch. Does it? Try it yourself. Also try stopping the fundamental by touching the wire at its mid-point with the card as before. Do you hear the second overtone clearly now?

Remember that the quality of the tone produced by a stretched string depends on the point where the string is plucked. Some overtones add brilliance to the fundamental, others, shrillness; some overtones thicken the tone, while others make it sound hollow.

Tone Quality

1. A simple sonometer.

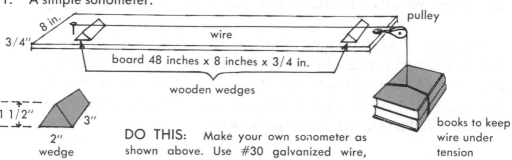

8 in.

3/4"

pulley

wire

board 48 inches x 8 inches x 3/4 in.

wooden wedges

books to keep wire under tension

1 1/2"

3"

2"

wedge

DO THIS: Make your own sonometer as shown above. Use #30 galvanized wire, sometimes called "flower wire," and available at hardware stores. Pulleys, called awning pulleys, are also sold at hardware stores. The wedges are about 1 1/2" x 2" x 3". If you can get it, use steel wire, called piano wire.

2.

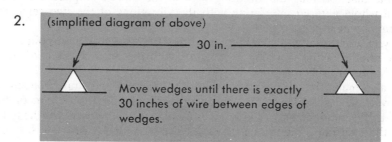

(simplified diagram of above)

30 in.

Move wedges until there is exactly 30 inches of wire between edges of wedges.

DO THIS: Keep wire taut by the pull of one or more books tied to end of wire that passes over pulley as shown above. Now pluck your 30 inch wire in the middle. Listen to the note produced. Do this several times. Do you see the wire vibrating as a whole, in one large loop? Your wire is emitting its *fundamental*, which is the lowest note it can produce.

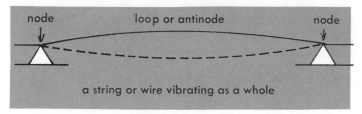

node

loop or antinode

node

a string or wire vibrating as a whole

3.

Make your wire vibrate in two equal segments by plucking it at one-quarter of its length from one end — i.e., at the 7 1/2-inch mark.

pluck at 7 1/2" mark

Listen to the tone. Is it higher than when wire was plucked in middle? You are hearing the fundamental and the first overtone. Now *while* wire is vibrating, touch middle or 15-inch mark *lightly* with edge of a card. This will stop the vibration of the fundamental and you will hear the first overtone distinctly.

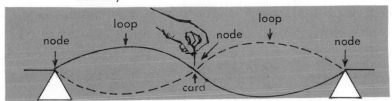

String or wire vibrating in two equal segments. Frequency of each segment is *twice* that of fundamental. The note you hear is therefore an octave higher than the fundamental. Explain. It is called the *first* overtone.

4. How does the above string vibrate when it is plucked at the one-quarter mark and *not* touched in the exact middle with a card?

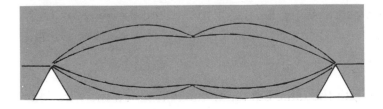

Shows wire simultaneously emitting its fundamental and first overtone. You hear a mixture of the two tones. Is the *quality* different from the fundamental by itself? From the first overtone by itself? Try it several times. Explain.

5.

To make the wire vibrate in three equal segments, try plucking it at a point *one-sixth* of its length from one end and quickly touch it with the edge of a card a a point *one-third* of its length from the end. You will then hear

the second overtone, given forth by the three equal vibrating segments. Each segment will be vibrating at three times the frequency of the fundamental, which you stopped with the card.

facts and ideas about . . .

The Laws of Vibrating Strings

You are going to use your sonometer to find out how stringed instruments can produce tones of different frequencies and therefore of different pitch. Remember that throughout the experiment you will work with *fundamentals,* with the strings or wires vibrating as a *whole* on being plucked *in the middle.* This will make the results easier to understand.

To perform this experiment accurately you should have two tuning forks, one which will vibrate at 256 vps and the other at 512 vps. You could then *tune* the string or wire to one of these forks and then to the other fork to detect a doubling or halving of frequency.

Since you probably lack these tuning forks, we shall rely on pitch, on what *you hear.* Keep in mind that pitch depends mainly on frequency of vibration: the higher the frequency, the higher the pitch; the lower the frequency, the lower the pitch.

You will listen to the note emitted by a vibrating, stretched wire of a certain length. Then decrease the length of this particular wire by half. What do you notice about the pitch of the vibrating wire when the length is halved?

Try keeping the length the same but make the tension on the wire four times greater. What change in pitch do you detect? Be sure to pluck the wire in the middle each time.

You will compare the pitch of the notes emitted by two *different* wires, one thicker and heavier than the other. More exactly, one string will have a different *mass per unit length* than the other. The wires will of course be of the same length and under the same tension — i.e., subject to the same stretching force. Which one produces a note of higher pitch — the thick or the thin wire?

The laws of vibrating strings may be expressed as follows:

(a) Frequency varies *inversely* as the length. Do you see why we say "inversely"?
(b) Frequency varies *directly* as the *square root* of the tension. This means that the tension must be made *four times greater* in order to *double* the frequency. Do you see why? ($\sqrt{4} = 2$)
(c) Frequency varies *inversely* as the square root of the mass per unit length. This means that if a thick string has *four times* the density or mass per unit length of a thin string, the frequency of the thick string will be half that of the thin string.

What the laws of vibrating strings mean to *your ear and brain:*

> Short strings emit notes of high pitch.
> Tightly stretched strings emit notes of high pitch.
> Light strings emit notes of high pitch.
> Long strings emit notes of low pitch.
> Loose strings emit notes of low pitch.
> Heavy strings emit notes of low pitch.

Think of the strings on a violin. The strings are of different thicknesses. The G string is the heaviest and produces the lowest frequency or pitch. The performer changes the tension, and therefore the pitch, by tightening or loosening the strings when he *"tunes"* his instrument. He also changes the effective lengths of the strings with his fingers while playing. How does this change the pitch?

Laws of Strings

1. Length.

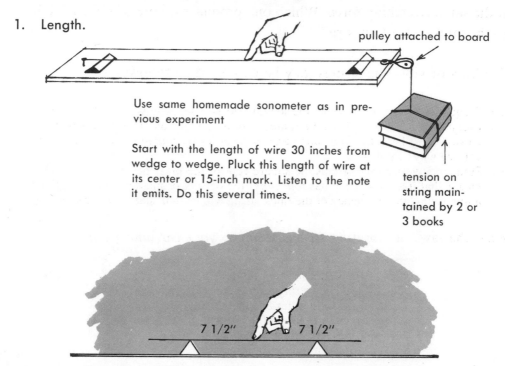

pulley attached to board

Use same homemade sonometer as in previous experiment

Start with the length of wire 30 inches from wedge to wedge. Pluck this length of wire at its center or 15-inch mark. Listen to the note it emits. Do this several times.

tension on string maintained by 2 or 3 books

7 1/2"   7 1/2"

Now reduce wire length between wedges to half, or 15 inches. Keep same tension. Pluck at middle, or 7 1/2 inches from wedges. Listen to the note emitted. Is it of a higher or lower pitch? Do you think the frequency of vibration increases or decreases as the wire is shortened? Try making the vibrating wire still shorter. Listen to the pitch of the note.

2. Tension.

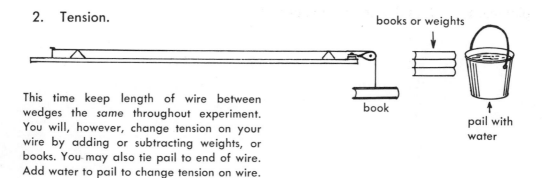

books or weights

book

pail with water

This time keep length of wire between wedges the *same* throughout experiment. You will, however, change tension on your wire by adding or subtracting weights, or books. You may also tie pail to end of wire. Add water to pail to change tension on wire.

Try one book, then two, three, etc., at the end of your wire. This changes the tension on the wire.

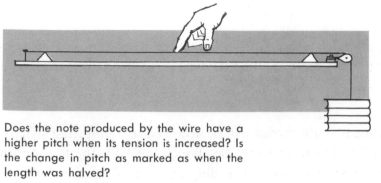

Compare the note emitted when 1 book is used with the note emitted when 4 books are used. Try to get books of about same weight. Also try using 2 similar wires across wedges at same time, each under a different tension.

Does the note produced by the wire have a higher pitch when its tension is increased? Is the change in pitch as marked as when the length was halved?

3. Mass per unit length. You will compare light and heavy strings whose length and tension are the *same*.

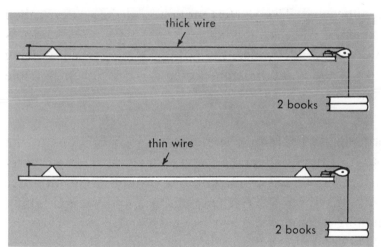

thick wire

2 books

thin wire

2 books

Same length, same tension, *but* different thickness or *mass per unit* length.

Use the #30 galvanized "flower" wire as your *thin* wire. Get a roll of *stove-pipe* wire or any wire of thickness #18 or #20, and use it as your *thick* wire.

Try plucking each wire. Which produces a note of a higher pitch? Be sure there is a *noticeable* difference in thickness between the wires you use.

facts and ideas about . . .

Melde's Experiment

You are going to make a thread vibrate in two, and then in three segments by using the ingenious method devised in 1859 by F. E. Melde, a German physicist.

In this experiment a silk thread will be attached to a vibrating strip of metal. The length of the thread may be changed at will; the tension on the thread may be varied easily. The diagrams and directions explain how this may be done.

When your thread vibrates as a whole, there is a point of *no motion,* called a *node,* at either end. The greatest motion is at the center, called an *anti-node*. The entire wave section between two *consecutive* nodes is called a *loop*. As pointed out earlier, the note produced when a string vibrates as a whole is called the *fundamental* and is the *lowest* possible note for that string.

In your experiment the vibrator communicates its vibrations to the thread attached to it. If the length and tension of the thread are properly adjusted, you will see the thread divide into one or more loops in order to keep in step with the vibrator. Try changing the length while keeping a minimum stretching weight at the end of the thread. Do you see the thread divide into fairly large loops or vibrating segments?

After trying various lengths of thread at random, you will turn to the more exact part of your experiment. Attach four small weights to the end of the thread. Adjust the length until you see the thread vibrating as *one large loop*. The thread is now vibrating at its fundamental frequency and is in step or resonance with the vibrator.

Now without changing the length of the thread, remove *three* of the small weights from the end of the thread. This means that the tension on the thread will now be *one-quarter* of what it was before. The frequency of the vibrating thread, with length unchanged, will now be one *one-half* of what it was before. Why? ($\sqrt{\frac{1}{4}} = \frac{1}{2}$; also see page 57.)

Before the change in tension, your thread kept in step by vibrating as a whole. How will it keep in step when the tension is reduced as above? Try it.

You will see *two* segments or loops form where only *one* was present before. Why? The thread vibrating as a *whole cannot* keep in step. It has to divide into two equal parts or segments. Since each half has twice the frequency of the whole thread (see page 52), the two *halves* keep in step with the vibrator even though the thread vibrating as a whole *cannot* keep in step. Think about this.

Review facts: In musical instruments, the notes produced by vibrating segments are called *overtones* or *harmonics*. When a string vibrates in two segments, it gives out its first overtone (second harmonic); when it vibrates in three segments, it produces its second overtone (third harmonic).

Notes about the experiments that follow: Try darkening the room and flashing a light along the vibrating thread. The pulsating loops make a beautiful sight. Also try to obtain three loops in your vibrating thread by changing the tension from nine small weights to one — i.e., the frequency of the thread vibrating as a *whole* will be reduced to one-third of what it was before ($\sqrt{\frac{1}{9}} = \frac{1}{3}$).

Melde's Experiment

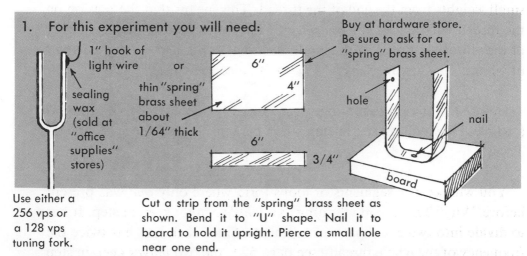

1. For this experiment you will need:

1" hook of light wire or thin "spring" brass sheet about 1/64" thick

sealing wax (sold at "office supplies" stores)

6"
4"

6"   3/4"

Buy at hardware store. Be sure to ask for a "spring" brass sheet.

hole

nail

board

Use either a 256 vps or a 128 vps tuning fork.

Cut a strip from the "spring" brass sheet as shown. Bend it to "U" shape. Nail it to board to hold it upright. Pierce a small hole near one end.

2.

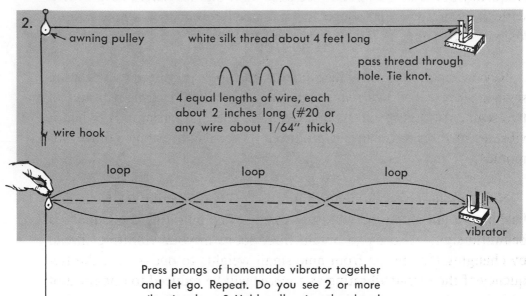

awning pulley

white silk thread about 4 feet long

pass thread through hole. Tie knot.

4 equal lengths of wire, each about 2 inches long (#20 or any wire about 1/64" thick)

wire hook

loop   loop   loop

vibrator

weight of wire produces tension

Press prongs of homemade vibrator together and let go. Repeat. Do you see 2 or more vibrating loops? Hold pulley in other hand or attach it to a stick. Change length of vibrating thread by moving the pulley closer or further from your vibrator. Can you get the thread to vibrate as a whole — i.e., with only one loop? Try it. Also try darkening room and using a flashlight to illuminate the loops.

3.

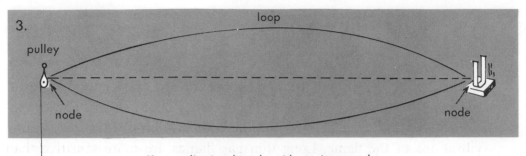

pulley

loop

node

node

Use 4 weights to supply tension to string, or 4 wires, or 4 small washers

Keep adjusting length, with tension equal to 4 wires, till the thread vibrates as a whole — i.e., one loop. How long your vibrating thread will be depends on the frequency of your vibrator, the tension on the string, the thickness of the thread, etc. Measure the length of the thread when you get the *single* loop.

4.

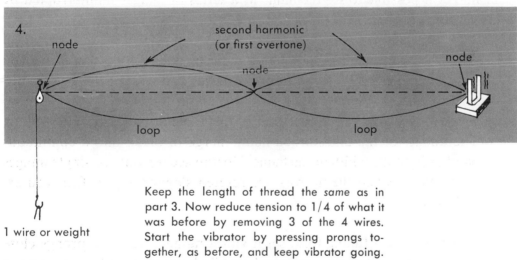

second harmonic (or first overtone)

node

node

node

loop

loop

1 wire or weight

Keep the length of thread the *same* as in part 3. Now reduce tension to 1/4 of what it was before by removing 3 of the 4 wires. Start the vibrator by pressing prongs together, as before, and keep vibrator going. Do you see two loops? Reducing tension by 1/4 changes the natural frequency of the *whole* thread by 1/2. Explain. See p. 57. The thread cannot keep up with the vibrator, so it divides into two segments or loops. This division produces the second harmonic or first overtone.

facts and ideas about . . .

Vibrating Flames

You are going to use a funnel and rubber tube to direct sound waves at the lower part of a candle flame. The series of compressions and expansions set up in the air by the vibrating body will produce corresponding vibrations of the flame. Long thin gas flames are more sensitive than candle flames, but you should be able to obtain interesting wave patterns with the latter if you follow the simple directions on the next page.

If you look at a vibrating flame directly, it is impossible to see the vibrations because they are too rapid. Rotating mirrors, however, serve to spread out the images of a disturbed or flaring flame so that one can see the wave form or pattern produced by a sound. Persistence of vision makes it possible to see the flame as a series of images uninterrupted by the edges of the mirror block.

It is best to begin by practicing with an undisturbed flame. As you rotate the mirror block at a uniform speed, you will see across the mirrors a horizontal band of light with a smooth top edge. Why? Since no sound waves are being directed at it, the flame does not vibrate or flare. The images of the undisturbed flame merge or blend into a continuous band of light the width of the flame. Do you see separate or single images of the flame when the mirrors are rotated slowly? Try it. Can you explain why?

If you have a tuning fork, set it vibrating and bring the prongs close to the funnel end of the rubber tube while holding the other end next to the flame. A tuning fork is one of the few musical instruments that produces a pure tone — only the fundamental is present. (See page 52.) The tone emitted by a tuning fork appears in the rotating mirrors as a series of equally spaced saw-teeth or serrations, all of the same length.

Can you explain this? See what you get with an ordinary vibrating fork placed next to the funnel.

As we learned in the experiment on tone quality (see page 52) practically all musical sounds consist of a mixture of tones of different pitches. The richness of the tones of musical instruments as well as of the human voice is due to the presence of a number of higher-pitched sounds, called overtones, in addition to the fundamental. Suppose, to take a simple case, a string is emitting simultaneously a fundamental with a frequency of 200 vps and an overtone with a frequency of 400 vps. A flame set into vibration by this sound combination will appear in the rotating mirrors with two saw-teeth or serrations, one longer than the other.

Further experiments with your rotating mirrors:

(a) You will try *singing* the vowel sound in the word *bee* into the funnel. This sound has two intense overtones, one with a frequency of about 300 vps and another of about 3,000 vps. Do you see at least two saw-teeth of unequal lengths in the mirrors? Try it. Can you explain this wave form?
(b) The vowel sound in the word *gloom* has a distinct overtone with a frequency of about 300 vps. Try singing it into the funnel. How many saw-teeth do you observe in the mirrors? Also try singing the vowel sound *a* in the word *father*. This sound has a strong overtone with a frequency of about 925 vps. How many saw-teeth in the image this time?

At one time sensitive flames were used in investigations of the relation of tone quality to wave form. Nowadays the cathode-ray oscilloscope, a far superior tool, has been applied together with a microphone to the study of complex sound waves. The wave forms appearing on the screen of the oscilloscope are then photographed.

65

Vibrating Flames

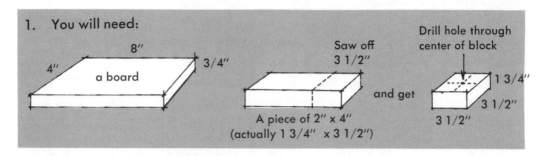

1. You will need:

8"
4"
3/4"
a board

Saw off
3 1/2"

A piece of 2" x 4"
(actually 1 3/4" x 3 1/2")

and get

Drill hole through
center of block

1 3/4"
3 1/2"
3 1/2"

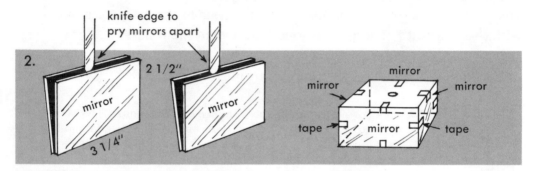

2.

knife edge to
pry mirrors apart

2 1/2"
mirror
mirror
3 1/4"

mirror
mirror
mirror
mirror
tape
tape

DO THIS: Pry apart two double pocket mirrors and get four small rectangular mirrors. Mount on sides of block as shown, using cellophane tape to hold mirrors in place.

Four mirrors, facing outward, one on each side of block. A drilled hole passes through center of block.

3.

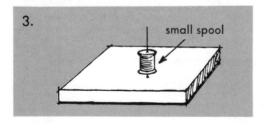

small spool

Hammer long nail through center of board from bottom. Slip a small spool over nail.

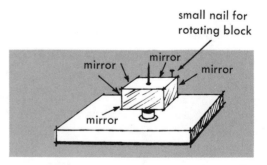

small nail for
rotating block

mirror
mirror
mirror
mirror

Here is your rotating block with four mirrors, one on each side. The spool reduces friction.

4.

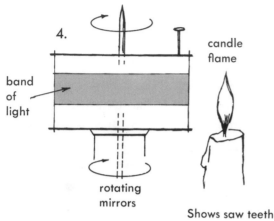

band
of
light

rotating
mirrors

candle
flame

Place a candle flame in front of mirror block. Do you see flame image? Now rotate mirror block slowly, then rapidly. Do you see a band of light? Do the flame images merge while mirrors are rotating rapidly? Why?

Shows saw teeth
or serrations
caused by a
complex sound.

cardboard or
paper funnel

narrow rubber tube

5.

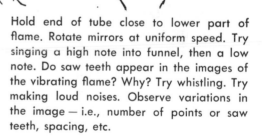

Hold end of tube close to lower part of flame. Rotate mirrors at uniform speed. Try singing a high note into funnel, then a low note. Do saw teeth appear in the images of the vibrating flame? Why? Try whistling. Try making loud noises. Observe variations in the image — i.e., number of points or saw teeth, spacing, etc.

Shows fundamental
and overtones in a
musical note.

6. Blow a toy flute or a whistle into the funnel while mirrors are rotating. Do you see a regularly repeated pattern? Why? How does a musical note differ from a noise?

7. Try singing the vowel sound in *gloom* into the funnel. Do your mirrors show a wave pattern similar to the one shown?

gloom

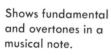

father

Try singing the *a* in *father* into the funnel. Do you get a wave pattern somewhat like the one shown?

Repeat these and other vowel sounds many times and observe wave patterns in mirrors.

facts and ideas about . . .

Musical Intervals

You are going to blow gently and steadily across the tops of tubes of different lengths. These air-filled tubes will be open at both ends and of the *same* diameter. You will listen carefully to the note emitted by each when the air column within it is set into vibration by the stream of air you blow across the top.

If one of your tubes is twice as long as another, then the air column in the first tube must be twice as long as the air column in the second. The longer the tube or pipe, the lower the fundamental frequency or pitch of the note produced.

Think about this: Suppose one tube is twice as long as another. Their length ratio will be 1 to 2. You set the air columns in these tubes vibrating by blowing across the top of each. The frequencies of vibration of the two *notes* you hear are in the ratio of 2 to 1. Why? Because the *shorter* the tube of air, the *higher* the frequency of the tone it will produce. Try this.

Early in human history musicians discovered that two tones were *most harmonious* sounded *together* when they were an *octave* apart. A tone is said to be an *octave higher* if it has a vibration frequency *twice* that of another tone. We know now that this is the simplest possible vibration ratio, namely 2 to 1. The exact number of vibrations does not matter; the important fact is that one note has *double* the vps or frequency of another note.

Ratios like 2 to 1, 3 to 2, 4 to 3, 5 to 4, etc. (usually written as 2/1, 3/2, 4/3, 5/4) each express the *musical interval* between *two* notes. The ratio 4/3, for example, tells us that the larger frequency is 4/3 times the smaller frequency.

You will make the length of one tube *twice* the length of another tube. The length ratio is therefore 1 to 2. This means the vibration ratio of the tones emitted by the two different air columns will be in the ratio of 2 to 1. Why? Blow across the ends of both tubes at the *same* time. Are the two tones, an octave apart, harmonious? Try this.

You will now use two tubes whose lengths are in the ratio of 2 to 3, as explained on the experiment page. Their vibration ratio is therefore 3 to 2. Why? Do they make a harmonious combination when sounded together?

Now try a 3 to 4 length ratio. The vibration ratio of the air columns will be 4 to 3. Do they make a harmonious combination when sounded together?

Must intervals always be expressed by small, whole numbers? No. But the most harmonious combinations are those that may be expressed by small, whole numbers. Try making one tube 4½ inches long and another 5 inches long. The length ratio is 9 to 10. Why? The vibration ratio is 10 to 9. Sound the tones together. Are they harmonious?

Finally adjust the lengths of *three tubes* so that their length ratios will be 6:5:4. The vibration ratios will be 4:5:6. Sound the tones *together*. Any *three* tones whose vibration ratios are 4 to 5 to 6 produce a remarkably *pleasing* combination when sounded together. Try it. This combination is now called a perfect *major chord*. Human beings recognized this pleasing combination of tones long before they knew about vibration ratios.

Musical Intervals

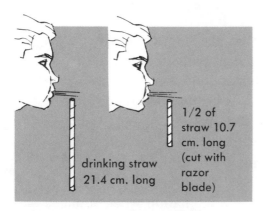

1/2 of straw 10.7 cm. long (cut with razor blade)

drinking straw 21.4 cm. long

length ratio is 1:2 (ratio of shorter length to longer length)
vibration ratio is 2:1
corresponds to do, do'

1.

Use 1/4-inch copper tubing, or glass tubes, or plastic tubes, or drinking-straw tubes.

You now have two air columns whose length ratio is 1 to 2.
Blow across the top of each. You will hear two notes, a high-pitch note from the short tube and a low-pitch note from the long tube. As in the case of strings, the vibration frequency or pitch varies inversely as the length of the air column.

2.

The *interval* in the above is usually expressed as 2:1 or 2. This is the simplest possible ratio between two notes. They are an *octave* apart. Sound them together. Is the combination pleasing or harmonious?

3.

Now prepare two tubes whose vibration ratios are 3:2, or 3/2. (The ratio of the larger frequency to the smaller.) The interval now is 3:2.

Cut a straw to obtain a piece which is 2/3 the length of a complete straw or 14.3 cm. Now you have 2 air columns whose length ratio is 2:3. When set vibrating, the vibration ratio will be the inverse, or 3:2. Sound each separately and then together. Is the combination pleasing, harmonious?

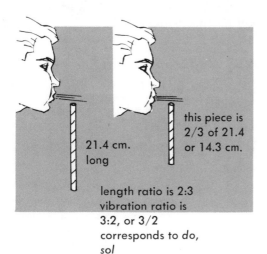

21.4 cm. long

this piece is 2/3 of 21.4 or 14.3 cm.

length ratio is 2:3
vibration ratio is 3:2, or 3/2
corresponds to *do, sol*

4. Now cut tubes to proper length to get the *do, mi* interval, which is 5:4.

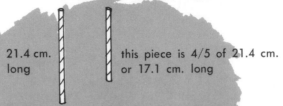

21.4 cm. long

this piece is 4/5 of 21.4 cm. or 17.1 cm. long

length ratio is 4:5
vibration ratio is 5:4 or 5/4
corresponds to *do, mi*

The 5:4 or 5/4 interval is another harmonious interval. Sound the two notes separately and then together. Is the combination pleasing to your ear? Note, once again, that 5/4 expresses the ratio of the larger frequency to the smaller.

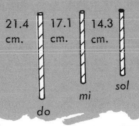

21.4 cm.   17.1 cm.   14.3 cm.

sol

mi

do

vibration ratios   1   5/4   3/2

           (4)   (5)   (6)

5. The three notes *do, mi, sol* sounded together form the major *triad*, a remarkably pleasing combination of tones. Try them together.

To understand the figures below diagrams, note the following: Vibration ratios 1, 5/4, 3/2 are same as 4/4, 5/4, 6/4. These three notes therefore have vibration ratios of 4:5:6.

facts and ideas about . . .

The Major Scale

You are going to add four tubes to the four you prepared in the previous experiment. These additional tubes will be of such length that they will fill in the missing intervals. Altogether you will then have eight tubes, each of a different length but with the same diameter. By blowing across these tubes one at a time, when they are lined up according to length, you should be able to produce the *major scale*.

You may use tubes of plastic, cardboard, metal, etc. You do not have to start, as in the experiment, with a tube 21.4 cm. long. You may begin with the first tube of any convenient length — 30 cm., 45 cm., 100 cm., etc.

Suppose you start with a 50-cm. tube. Call this tube *do*. Now cut or reduce the length of a second tube so that it will be 8/9 of 50 cm. This will give you the correct length for *re*. Now reduce the length of a third tube to 4/5 of 50 cm. This will give you the correct length for *mi*. See experiment page for other length ratios.

In regular concert organs, the tubes are as short as 6 inches for the *highest* note, and nearly 16 feet for the *lowest* note.

Remember that an experienced musician learns to measure a musical interval by *ear*. To him, an interval is the *difference in pitch* between two notes. A physicist, on the other hand, measures a musical interval by the *ratio* of the *vibration frequencies* of the two notes. Think about this.

(a) Pythagoras, a Greek philosopher and mathematician, who died about 500 B.C., is said to have investigated the consonance of musical sounds by experimenting with vibrating strings. He discovered that the most harmonious combinations were produced when a string was divided into two parts with length ratios of 2:1, 3:1, 3:2, and 4:3. Pythagoras concluded that the simpler the ratio of the lengths of the parts of a string, the more perfect the consonance, that is, the more harmonious the combination of the two sounds.

(b) It was Galileo (1564-1642), the Italian astronomer and physicist, who, about two thousand years after Pythagoras, discovered the relationship between the length of a string and its frequency of vibration. (See laws of strings on page 57). The frequency of vibration of a stretched string is inversely proportional to its length. In the experiment that follows, do you see why we must invert the length ratios in order to obtain the vibration ratios?

(c) The term *diatonic* is derived from the Greek word meaning *to stretch*. In modern music, diatonic designates the standard major or minor scale consisting of eight tones to an octave.

A chord (derived from the word *accord*) consists of two or more notes which combine or blend harmoniously when sounded together. Any three notes whose vibration ratios are 4:5:6 produce a major chord when sounded together. Thus the three major chords have vibration ratios of 4:5:6. Try these major cords on your piano or use your home-made tubes:

> The chord *do-mi-sol* is called the tonic.
> The chord *sol-ti-re* is called the dominant.
> The chord *fa-la-do'* is called the subdominant.

As pointed out in the previous experiment, certain intervals expressed by larger whole numbers are *discordant*. Such tones do not blend harmoniously. Try sounding together the *do* and *re* of your tubes. The interval is 9/8 or 9:8. Is the combination pleasing to the ear?

Notes about the experiment that follows: The figures and calculations on the next two pages may appear confusing at first. Go over the directions and explanations slowly several times and they will become more understandable.

Can you produce the scale, using the air columns in eight tall jars with straight sides? Try calculating the correct lengths of the air columns. Add different amounts of water to each jar to get the proper lengths.

The Major Diatonic Scale

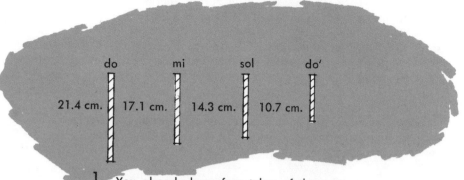

1. You already have four tubes of the proper lengths. They produce notes corresponding to *do, mi, sol, do'* of the major scale. Let us prepare other tubes, cut to the correct lengths, so that we may sound the complete scale, from *do* to *do'*.

2. Here are the vibration ratios of the notes in major diatonic scale:

	do	re	mi	fa	sol	la	ti	do'
letters	C	D	E	F	G	A	B	C'
vibration ratios	1	9/8	5/4	4/3	3/2	5/3	15/8	2

3. You will continue to work with *length* ratios, which are the *inverse* of vibration ratios. To prevent confusion, the length ratios will be expressed, once again, as the ratio of the *shorter* length to the *longer* length.

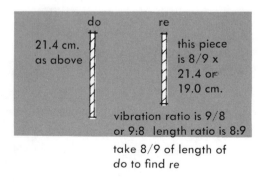

vibration ratio is 9/8
or 9:8 length ratio is 8:9

take 8/9 of length of
do to find *re*

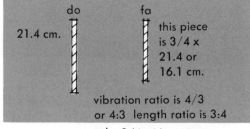

vibration ratio is 4/3
or 4:3 length ratio is 3:4

take 3/4 of length of
do to find *fa*

4. Let's make the *la* and *ti* tubes

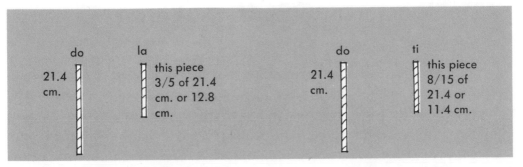

do
21.4 cm.

la
this piece 3/5 of 21.4 cm. or 12.8 cm.

do
21.4 cm.

ti
this piece 8/15 of 21.4 or 11.4 cm.

vibration ratio is 5:3
length ratio is 3:5
take 3/5 of length of
do to find *la*.

vibration ratio is 15:8
length ratio is 8:15
take 8/15 of *do* to
find *ti*

5.

Now line up the 8 tubes and blow across them in order of length. Insert tubes in a cardboard holder if drinking straws were used. Pierce holes in cardboard holder.

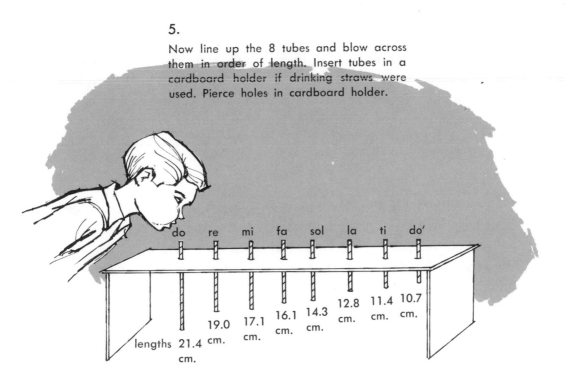

do   re   mi   fa   sol   la   ti   do'

lengths 21.4 cm.   19.0 cm.   17.1 cm.   16.1 cm.   14.3 cm.   12.8 cm.   11.4 cm.   10.7 cm.

facts and ideas about . . .

The Vibrations of Rods and Wires

You are going to set up *transverse* waves in a long steel rod by striking it near the middle with a piece of wood or with a rubber mallet. The particles in the rod move back and forth from their rest positions at right angles to the length of the rod; the disturbance travels *along* the length of the rod. Do you see why we call this wave, or disturbance, transverse?

To see how the rod vibrates, you will look directly at the free end while the rod is vibrating. But first attach a small glass bead to the free end, using chewing gum to hold the bead in place. Now, in a darkened room, illuminate the bead with a flashlight. Set the rod vibrating as before. You will see the shining point of light describe interesting figures or curves. Try it.

This arrangement of vibrating rod, bead, and light is called a *kaleido-phone*. It was devised by Charles Wheatstone (1802-1875), an English physicist. The word is derived from the Greek: *kalos* meaning beautiful, *eidos* meaning form, and *phōnē* meaning sound. The figures you will see are called Lissajous figures, after the French scientist, J. A. Lissajous (1822-1880).

Your illuminated bead will move in straight lines, ellipses, and circles, and these will keep changing and revolving in a most striking fashion. Why don't you get just one kind of figure as the rod vibrates transversely? Because the steel rod is neither perfectly round nor perfectly uniform all along its length. Also its elasticity is not the same in every direction. These imperfections account for the changing, revolving figures.

Wooden rods of different lengths are found in the xylophone. When struck near the center, *transverse* vibrations are set up in the rods. The shorter rods produce the high notes and the longer rods the low notes. A *tuning fork* may be regarded as made up of two parallel bars clamped together at the base; it depends upon the *transverse* vibrations of the parallel bars for its pitch.

You will also set the long steel rod into *longitudinal* vibration. You can do this by stroking it in the direction of its *length* with a moist cloth. This time the particles move back and forth in the direction along which the wave or disturbance is traveling — i.e., the *length* of the rod. Listen to the note emitted by the rod when stroked. This note is fairly close to the fundamental of the rod.

Finally, try stretching a thin wire, about 15 feet long, across your room. Get it fairly taut and attach the ends to two nails or hooks. Now stroke this long wire near the middle with a moist cloth. Are you setting up *transverse* or *longitudinal vibrations?* Listen to the note produced by stroking. Is this note the fundamental of your wire? Try *plucking* the wire at the middle. Compare the pitch of the two notes — one produced by longitudinal vibrations and the other by transverse vibrations.

Try stroking your wire near the quarter-length mark. Do you hear a higher or lower note than when the wire was stroked in the middle? Can you explain it? You have produced the first overtone. Now try producing the first overtone by transverse vibrations (see page 16). Compare the two notes.

Vibrations of Rods

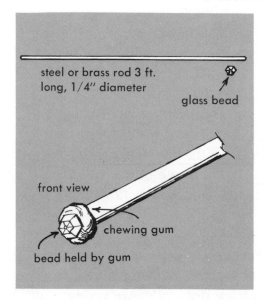

steel or brass rod 3 ft. long, 1/4" diameter

glass bead

front view

chewing gum

bead held by gum

1. Wheatstone's kaleidophone.

Get a 3-foot, 1/4"-diameter rod in hardware store. The solid, brass-plated rods used for hanging drapes will do. Dig a small glass bead out of a piece of cheap costume jewelry. Try to get a bead with sharp edges. Attach bead to end of rod with chewing gum. Clamp one end of rod in a vise.

2. Transverse vibrations of rods.

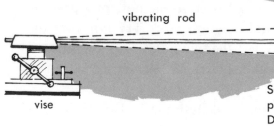

vibrating rod

flashlight

bead

vise

Set the rod into *transverse* vibration by tapping it in middle with a small piece of wood. Darken the room. Illuminate the bead with a flashlight. Do you see the shining bead vibrate? Notice the figures or curves the bead describes as it vibrates. These striking figures are called *Lissajous* figures. Do the figures seem to revolve?

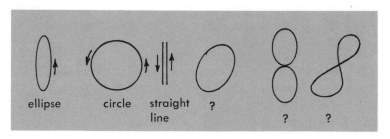

ellipse   circle   straight line   ?   ?   ?

Do you see these? Try tapping different parts of the rod.

3. Longitudinal vibrations of rods.

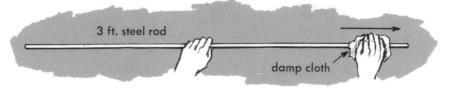

Hold your rod in the middle with one hand. Now stroke one end *outward* with a damp cloth, starting about 3 inches from this end. Do you hear a note? The rod is vibrating back and forth *longitudinally*.

4. Longitudinal vibrations in a thin wire.

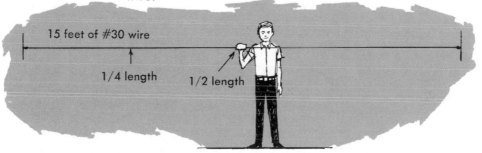

Stretch a wire, about 15 feet long, across a room. Attach to hooks or nails. The #30 galvanized iron wire used in the experiment on laws of strings will do.

With a damp cloth stroke this stretched wire over one foot of the middle section *one way*. Do you hear a definite note? This is the *fundamental* of your wire.

Now stroke the wire at its *quarter* length mark with your damp cloth. Is the note produced *higher* than the fundamental? You should hear the first overtone. Try stroking the stretched wire at other points, too.

facts and ideas about . . .

The Xylophone

You are going to investigate the transverse vibrations (see page 16) of rods such as are used in percussion instruments like the xylophone and marimba. The former consists of wooden rods of varying length. The word xylophone is derived from the Greek *xylon,* meaning wood and *phōnē,* sound or voice.

In your experiments you will use copper pipes or tubes, for these behave like solid rods or bars when set into transverse vibration by a sharp blow at or near their centers. Copper or brass tubing is inexpensive, available everywhere, and easy to cut into exact lengths.

The pitch of the note produced when a rod or tube is struck depends on how it is supported. You will first try resting the copper tube on two supports, each .22 or approximately one-fifth of the tube length from each end. This tube, when struck in the middle, will then emit its lowest note or fundamental (see page 52). Then move the two supports so that they are nearer the ends of the tube. Also move them so that they are closer to the middle of the tube. Can you get a tone lower in pitch than when the supports are at the one-fifth points? Try it.

When supported near the ends, that is, at the one-fifth marks, a tube or rod vibrates in the manner shown in the diagram on the next page. The center of the tube or rod moves up and down freely, as do the ends. These points of maximum vibration are called *loops;* the points of least or no vibration, called *nodes,* are about one-fifth of the length from each end. Do you see why it is important for vibrating rods or tubes to be supported at the node points?

Will a short tube emit a higher note than a long tube, in the manner

80

of stretched strings? You will rest two tubes of different lengths on rope or drinking-straw supports, as shown in the diagram on the next page. In which case is a higher note produced when the tubes are struck in the middle with a wooden hammer? Try this.

Finally you will saw or cut the copper tubing into the eight exact lengths described on the next page. You do not have to start with a 30-centimeter piece of tubing for *do*. You may begin with a shorter or longer length of tube for *do*. But the tube which will produce *re* must be 0.943 times the length of your *do* tube; the *mi* 0.894 times the length of your *do* tube, etc. Tie the tubes at the nodes with a strong cord as shown. If your measurements are accurate, the eight tubes will produce the musical scale when struck with a wooden hammer.

Interesting facts about the lengths of rods in a xylophone:

(a) In transverse vibration of uniform bars or rods or tubes, the frequency or number of vibrations per second of the notes emitted varies inversely as the square of the length. This means that you must make the tube *not* half as long to double its frequency, but $\sqrt{\frac{1}{2}}$ or 0.707 times as long. Thus the multiplier you will use to find the length of *do'* is 0.707 times the length of *do* — i.e., 0.707 times 30 centimeters in the experiment.

(b) Below are the different multipliers, based upon the above explanation. You will use them to find the lengths of the eight tubes that will produce the musical scale (see p. 72):

	do	re	mi	fa	sol	la	ti	do'
Scale Ratios	1	$\frac{9}{8}$	$\frac{5}{4}$	$\frac{4}{3}$	$\frac{3}{2}$	$\frac{5}{3}$	$1\frac{5}{8}$	2
Rod or tube lengths	$\sqrt{1}$	$\sqrt{\frac{8}{9}}$	$\sqrt{\frac{4}{5}}$	$\sqrt{\frac{3}{4}}$	$\sqrt{\frac{2}{3}}$	$\sqrt{\frac{3}{5}}$	$\sqrt{\frac{8}{15}}$	$\sqrt{\frac{1}{2}}$
Multipliers or square roots	1	0.943	0.894	0.866	0.815	0.774	0.730	0.707

The Xylophone

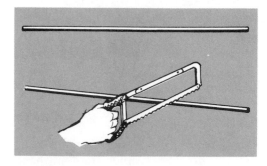

1. You will need:

1/4- or 1/2-inch copper tubing. Buy three 3-foot lengths at hardware or plumbing supply stores.

DO THIS: Begin by cutting off exactly 30 centimeters of tubing. Use a hacksaw or tubing cutter. The metric system is used in this experiment because the lengths are expressed as decimals for accuracy.

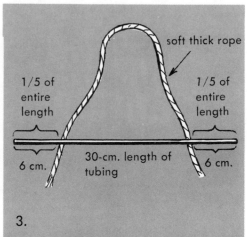

2. Transverse vibrations of bars, rods and tubes.

Lay 30-centimeter tube on rope as shown. Or use drinking straws under tube instead of rope. Strike middle of tube with wooden hammer or pencil. The note you hear is the *fundamental*, or lowest note this length of tubing can emit.
Try to get a lower note by moving tube up or down rope supports. Strike tube in middle. Can you get a *lower* note?

The tube vibrates transversely. Explain. The supports are located at the nodes. Why?

3.

How a bar, rod, or tube vibrates when struck in the middle.

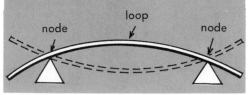

A vibrating tube or bar free at both ends has two nodes, each 0.22 of the entire length from the ends. This is the fundamental mode of vibration.

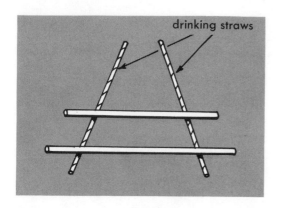

drinking straws

4. Length and Pitch:

Place a long tube and a short tube across rope or straws as shown. Be sure each tube is supported at the 1/5 points as before. Strike middle of each tube with wood part of pencil. Which produces a note of higher pitch — the long or short tube? Do these tubes behave like stretched strings? Explain.

5.

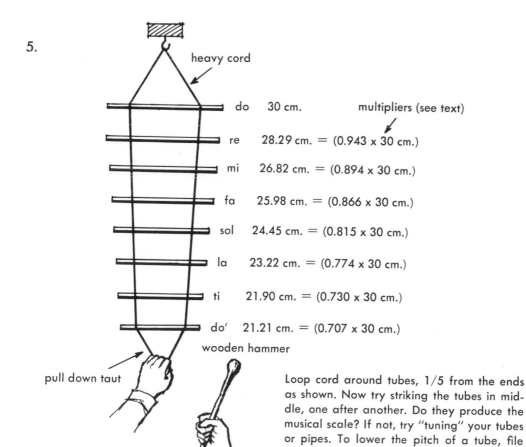

heavy cord

do	30 cm.	multipliers (see text)
re	28.29 cm.	= (0.943 x 30 cm.)
mi	26.82 cm.	= (0.894 x 30 cm.)
fa	25.98 cm.	= (0.866 x 30 cm.)
sol	24.45 cm.	= (0.815 x 30 cm.)
la	23.22 cm.	= (0.774 x 30 cm.)
ti	21.90 cm.	= (0.730 x 30 cm.)
do'	21.21 cm.	= (0.707 x 30 cm.)

wooden hammer

pull down taut

Loop cord around tubes, 1/5 from the ends as shown. Now try striking the tubes in middle, one after another. Do they produce the musical scale? If not, try "tuning" your tubes or pipes. To lower the pitch of a tube, file the middle of it a little at a time. To raise the pitch of a tube, file the ends. Why?

facts and ideas about . . .

Vibrations of Bell-Shaped Bodies

You are going to set a bell-shaped object like a wine glass into vibration by drawing a *wet* finger around its rim. After some practice you should succeed in obtaining a clear musical note from the vibrating wine glass as your wet finger goes round and round the circumference.

Each wine glass has its own natural frequency, which depends on its weight, shape, dimensions, quality of glass, and so forth. Will the pitch of the emitted note change when the vibrating wine glass has different amounts of water in it? Why? Try it with your glass.

You will add a few drops of ink to the water in the wine glass and then once again draw a wet finger around the rim. The vibrating colored water should enable you to see the bell-shaped glass divide into an even number of sectors while it is vibrating. Parts of the glass are contracting radially while others are dilating. Do the contracting sectors alternate with the dilating sectors? Study the disturbance in the colored water of your vibrating wine glass.

In your experiment the motion of the glass is not only inward and outward in reference to the radius, but also tangential. Tangential means that the sectors move around the wine glass as your wet finger goes round. Examine the moving pattern or figure on the surface of the water. Is there always a node under the moving finger? Or is there always a loop under it? Try it. Remember that a node is a point of no vibration, while a loop is a point of maximum vibration. Remember that nodes separate the sectors, and that there are usually four sectors in a vibrating bell. See diagram on next page.

You will repeat the above experiment this time with the wine glass immersed in a pail of water. Now the vibrating glass, the rim of which is slightly above water level, will have water both on its inside and outside. Do you see waves or a disturbance in the water outside the wine glass? Are sound waves transmitted by water? Is the pitch of the sound produced by drawing your wet finger around the rim different now? Explain.

An experiment similar to the last one was made at Lake Geneva in 1827. A bell was struck under water at the same time as a charge of gunpowder was flashed in the air above the bell. About 8 miles away a large ear-trumpet, with a membrane across the opening, was placed under water, with its tube extending above the surface. An observer above water, with his ear to the tube, noted the time interval between the arrival of the flash of light and the sound from the bell. The speed of sound in water is 4708 feet per second.

Interesting facts about bells:

(a) Large heavy bells, such as are used in churches, are cast and not riveted. They are made of bell-metal, which consists of a 4 to 1 mixture of copper and tin. The thickness of the bell's edge is about one-tenth its diameter; the height of the bell is twelve times its thickness. Bells are usually cuplike in shape; when struck, the main note emitted is the fundamental.
(b) Bell-ringing requires considerable experience and skill. The bell-ringer sets the bell ringing gradually. His first pull starts the pendulum-like swing of the bell. After a complete vibration or back-and-forth movement, the ringer gives the bell another pull just as it is starting on its downward path. He repeats his pulls in time with the moving bell. In this way he increases the amplitude of the swing until the bell is ringing as strongly as is desired. If the bell-ringer should apply his pulls at the wrong time, the bell would slow down or stop ringing. Why? Think of a swing pushed at the "wrong" time.

Vibrations of a Bell-Shaped Body

1. You will use a large wine glass. Add water to within 1/2 inch of rim. Add ink to the water in order to make the vibrations more visible.

2. Wet your finger. Now, pressing down firmly, draw wet finger around the edge of the wine glass. Keep moving wet finger round and round until you hear a clear shrill note. Don't stop when you hear the note, but keep going round and round.

3. Looking down into glass

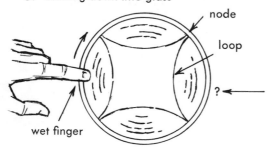

node

loop

wet finger

Do this several times.

Do you see four loops?
Do you see four nodes?

Does the figure move around with the finger?

4. Pour off some water and set the wine glass into vibration as before. Does the pitch of the note change? Why?

5.

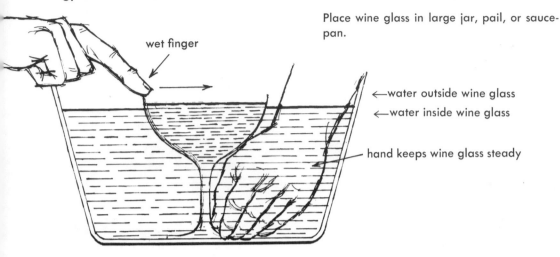

wet finger

Place wine glass in large jar, pail, or saucepan.

←water outside wine glass
←water inside wine glass

hand keeps wine glass steady

6.

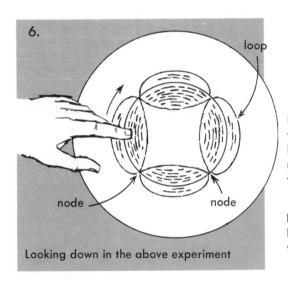

loop

node

node

Looking down in the above experiment

Draw finger round and round the edge of the wine glass until you hear a clear note. Don't stop. Keep the note sounding. Is there now a pattern, produced by the vibrating wine glass, on both sides of the glass?

Does pattern show an even number of nodes? Does the pattern or figure move with your finger?

Steady the wine glass by holding bottom down in pail with other hand.

7.

If you have a violin bow, try bowing the wine glass, containing water, at one point of its rim. Move bow down firmly and observe vibration pattern. Try this, of course, after removing wine glass from the pail or jar.

Further Reading

If you found certain subjects or topics in this book of particular interest, then why not go on to learn more about them? In other words, make a *learning project* out of your special interest. Use encyclopedias and textbooks for additional information and a deeper understanding. Wide reading will often turn up descriptions and diagrams of simple experiments you can try at home.

Get into the habit of using the index volume of an encyclopedia as well as the index pages of textbooks. Frequently a subject will be listed under a heading different from the one you may have in mind.

If the presentation in a particular encyclopedia is too detailed or difficult for you, search for a simpler explanation in another encyclopedia — and then go back to the more difficult one. Follow a similar procedure with textbooks: read a simplified explanation first, and then go on to one that is more advanced. Use more than one textbook; study the treatment of the same subject by different authors. Remember that if a book or explanation seems simple, you are probably ready for one that is more thorough, more challenging.

Standard Encyclopedias

Encyclopaedia Britannica, 1959.
Collier's Encyclopedia, 1962.
The Encyclopedia Americana, 1959.
Compton's Pictured Encyclopedia and Facts Index, 1962.
Van Nostrand's Scientific Encyclopedia, 1958.

There are many good textbooks in physics on the shelves of school and public libraries. If you cannot find the books listed below, other recently published physics texts will probably be as useful.

Bachman, C. H., *Physics*, Wiley, 1955.
Baker, D. L., R. B. Brownlee, and R. W. Fuller, *Elements of Physics*, Allyn and Bacon, 1955.
Blackwood, O. H., W. B. Herron, and W. C. Kelly, *Physics*, Ginn, 1958.
Brinkerhoff, R. F., et al., *Exploring Physics*, Harcourt, Brace, 1959.
Dull, C. E., H. C. Metcalfe, and J. E. Williams, *Modern Physics,* Holt, Rinehart and Winston, 1960.

Efron, Alexander, *Basic Physics*, Rider, 1958.

Elliott, L. P., and W. F. Wilcox, *Physics*, Macmillan, 1957.

Hausmann, E., and E. F. Slack, *Physics*, Van Nostrand, 1957.

Jeans, Sir James, *Science and Music*, Macmillan, 1940.

Knauss, H. P., *Discovering Physics*, Addison-Wesley, 1951.

Physics, Physical Science Study Committee, Heath, 1960.

Semat, Henry, *Physics in the Modern World,* Rinehart, 1949.

Taylor, L. W., *Physics, the Pioneer Science,* Houghton Mifflin, 1941 (an unusual approach to physics, rich in historical background).

White, H. E., *Modern College Physics*, Van Nostrand, 1957.

Glossary

AMPLITUDE — the greatest distance through which the particles of a vibrating body move from their rest positions.

ANTINODE — points of maximum vibration; the region of greatest motion or amplitude.

CHORD — the simultaneous sounding of two or more notes which combine or blend harmoniously.

CONDENSATION — a region of compression in a sound wave where the particles move in the direction of the wave.

DIFFRACTION — the bending of sound waves around obstacles.

DOPPLER EFFECT — the apparent change in pitch of a sound caused by the rapid change in the distance between source and observer.

ECHO — the distinct reflection of a short, sharp sound. The reflected sound can be distinguished from the original sound.

FREQUENCY — the number of complete vibrations in one second.

FUNDAMENTAL — in general, the lowest pitch that a source of musical tones can produce; a string vibrating as a whole emits its fundamental tone.

HARMONICS — tones whose vibration frequencies are whole-number multiples of the fundamental frequency; the fundamental is called the first harmonic.

INTENSITY — the amount of sound energy flowing through a unit area in one second.

LONGITUDINAL WAVES — waves in which the particles move back and forth in line with the motion of the wave.

LOOP — the entire wave section between two successive nodes.

LOUDNESS — a characteristic of a sound that depends upon the effect of the intensity of a sound wave on the ears.

MAJOR CHORD — the harmonious combination of three tones whose vibration ratios are 4, 5, and 6.

NODE — points of no motion or vibration, as at the ends of a vibrating string.

NOISE — a sound arising from vibrations whose frequencies are irregular or uneven.

OVERTONE — a tone whose vibration frequency is a whole-number multiple of the fundamental frequency; the first overtone is called the second harmonic.

PITCH — refers to the position of a tone on a musical scale and depends upon the frequency or number of sound impulses that strike the ear per second.

QUALITY — the characteristic of a musical sound that depends upon the overtones present and their prominence.

RAREFACTION — a region of reduced pressure in a sound wave where the particles move in a direction opposite to that of the wave.

REFRACTION — the change in direction of a sound wave when it passes from one medium into another in which its velocity is different.

RESONANCE — the response of a vibratory system at its natural frequency to impulses received from another vibrator having the same or a simple-multiple frequency.

REVERBERATION — the repeated reflection of sound resulting in the persistence or prolongation of the original sound.

SOUND — a vibratory disturbance in the air that produces the sensation of hearing.

TRANSVERSE WAVES — waves in which the particles move back and forth at right angles to the line of motion of the waves.

ULTRASONIC — vibrations in matter above the limits of audibility for human ears, that is, above 20,000 vps.

VIBRATIONS — repeated back-and-forth motion at a definite rate.

WAVE LENGTH — the distance between two corresponding points of any two successive waves; the distance between two successive wave crests; the distance between one condensation and the next.

Index

The Author

Harry Sootin is a New Yorker who has taught general science and physics in the New York City high schools for over twenty-five years. A graduate of the City College of New York, Mr. Sootin began his career as a chemist, and soon switched to teaching. He was a member of the faculty of the High School of Commerce in Manhattan, and then taught at Flushing High School on Long Island. He has always favored the laboratory approach to science teaching, believing that it is most effective in interesting his students in scientific facts and ideas.

In addition to his teaching duties, Mr. Sootin has devoted much of his time to writing. He is the author of some eight books for young people, including biographies of Isaac Newton, Michael Faraday, Gregor Mendel and Robert Boyle. Mr. Sootin has written many science articles for magazines as well as for the *Book of Knowledge*.

Harry Sootin is a member of the American Association for the Advancement of Science, the History of Science Society, and the Teachers Guild. He makes his home in Flushing, New York.